THE PIER

THE PIER

a novel by

RAYNER HEPPENSTALL

ALLISON & BUSBY

LONDON

First published in 1986 by
Allison & Busby Ltd
6a Noel Street, London W1V 3RB
and distributed in the USA by
Schocken Books Inc.,
62 Cooper Square, New York, NY 10003

British Library Cataloguing in Publication Data

Heppenstall, Rayner
   The pier.
   I. Title
   823'.912[F]   PR6015.E56

   ISBN 0-85031-450-X
   ISBN 0-85031-451-8 Pbk

Published with financial assistance from
the Arts Council of Great Britain

Set in 11/12½ Palatino by
Ann Buchan (Typesetters)
Printed and bound in Great Britain by
Billing and Sons Ltd, Worcester.

Contents

1 : The Way Home

AT LOW TIDE, the lower landing is barely awash. Water did not penetrate the welts of my shoes as, with the help of my ashplant, I stepped out, while Jean-Paul Richard held the boat steady by the mere friction of his fingertips on the concrete.

I have now climbed the first sixteen steps. I turn left about and climb sixteen more on this side of the pier, the southern side. There are no boats on the steep shingle or several hundred yards. Jean-Paul has started his engine and turned out to sea, which probably means he intends to spend the day fishing in English waters.

I am now on the upper deck of the pier, by the ladies' and gents' conveniences, the buffet and the bar, which will not be open for another four hours. There are no early morning walkers along the shingle on this side. There are no boatmen yet with their boats on the north side.

On all hands, the iron railings are painted a bright green, on all hands including the triangular areas of lower deck to either side of the pier at its very end, where they form three sides of a small square about each of ten great baulks of timber. The surface on which I stand and shall walk is a finely grained, green concrete. The plain concrete which supports the iron railings on either side of the main stretch of the pier is shaped into seating accommodation bottomed and backed with creosoted wood.

I can see the whole length of the town as far, to the right (which is to say to the south) at a point at which the land

7

turns away from the sea. To the right, as much as I think I can see of our growing residential suburb, once a separate township, lies in shadow. The sun rose just after Jean-Paul and I had rounded the last headland, but there won't be much sun today. Such light as comes from the east falls directly on the town.

This looks entirely charming, as towns do when seen from the sea, even in a poor light. As it is rather flat, I see buildings which lie on the sea front, before them boats and a great bank of shingle, which from here is uniformly golden yellow and rises quite evenly as far as the eye can see in either direction.

In fifty paces of the kind I take now, walking with a stick, I pass lamp-posts facing each other, set in the same concrete as the green iron railings. The lamps are of a peculiar, elongated shape which is not displeasing. After a little less than ninety paces, I come to shelters, again facing each other. In the one to the right hangs a lifebelt. To some of the lamp-posts, red litter-bins are affixed. About half-way along the pier, to a piece of the creosoted seat-backing is pasted a notice which reads: NO BAIT OR FISH TO BE PLACED ON SEATS.

On either side of the pier there are four shelters and nine lamp-posts. Past the last shelters, the railings are no longer painted green, but yellow. The change of colour indicates that no fishing should be done from the landward end of the pier. I should have taken this to be common sense and perhaps a warning to novice fishermen rather than a matter of official concern to the mayor and corporation, but what a notice at that point says is: FISHERMEN ARE NOTIFIED THAT BOATS HAVE RIGHT OF WAY WHERE RAILS ARE PAINTED YELLOW. The boats intended will be mainly skiffs of various lengths, out for rowing practice from the boathouse past the coastguard station, to the south and therefore to my right, which always keep close to the shore.

The whole length of the pier is four hundred and fifty

paces, short for a pier if you think of those of Brighton, Southend or Blackpool. At the landward end there is a ticket-office to the left, with no turnstile, but to the right a turnstile only, which presumably counts people leaving the pier. The numbering of the tickets would, if this were thought necessary, count those going on, but this would not be simple, as there are tickets of three values, *viz.*, 20 pence for the general run of visitors, 30 pence for those intending to fish and a mere 3 pence for children and old-age pensioners or, as we are called, senior citizens. My ticket would be pink if I had one. Between the buff and the white ones, I do not know what colours are sold to the other types of customer. In general, it is clear that the ticket-seller will distinguish intending fishermen by their rods, which are not easily concealed, though a man with a line in the pocket of a capacious overcoat would be able to get on the pier 10 pence cheaper as a visitor of the general run.

To my relief, whatever may usually be done with it, the turnstile was not locked last night. Had it been, I should, I feel sure, have been able to negotiate it, but I should have been conspicuous to anyone passing along the promenade or looking out of a seaward window.

Off the pier, I am on a horseshoe ramp of deeper green concrete enclosing a municipal flowerbed in which bloom such asters and dahlias as have escaped the depredations of children and of young men egged on by their girls. I pass in front of the headquarters of the Angling Association (if I had turned to the left, I should have passed the window of a seller of fishing tackle) and am presently on the plain concrete of Queen's Parade.

Across the road, immediately opposite, as though it had been carefully aligned with the pier entrance, stands the Albemarle hotel and restaurant. I turn right. The boats and winches displaced or damaged by the gales and flooding in January of last year have all now been restored to their places, mended or taken out of commission and replaced by visitors' boats.

9

At a hundred paces, I pass the *4 Brothers*, which was always there and undamaged, at two hundred the *Good Times*, sitting pretty opposite the Sun in Splendour, the town's oldest public house, now much modernised. At three hundred paces come the *Beau Jesse* and the notice-board which advertises piano recitals and dances at the Pavilion.

An unusually big boat, the *Lady Haig*, for long stood across the esplanade at four hundred paces, the *Maple Leaf* undisturbed at five hundred. There are, in all, forty-nine or fifty boats or places for boats in six hundred paces, my paces, say ten yards between boats.

ACROSS THE ROAD now rises the Metropole hotel, a splendid building suddenly condemned and abandoned last year because its fire precautions did not conform with new rules. Here, I must cross. Before I do so, I look out to sea in the hope of distinguishing Jean-Paul's boat, as I think I do.

Jean-Paul Richard is a man now, I suppose, in his late forties or early fifties, fair and rugged. I am fond of him.

How we first became acquainted is worth recalling. It is the earliest detail in the story now about to reach a climax of some kind. It must be understood that ten years ago I, Harold Atha, had no small reputation as an authority on French crime and French criminal trials, being, it seemed, the only English writer who committed no howlers about their legal procedure. This was the last phase in a long Francophily which has since declined for a variety of reasons, so that, until this year, I had not so much as crossed the Channel for eight or nine years.

One of our Sunday newspapers sent me to St Omer to cover the trial of Armand Rohart, mayor of Peuplingues, a small commune in the Pas de Calais, on a charge of having murdered his wife on the beach at Escalles, an equally small commune on the coast nearby. The trial was to start on July 2nd, 1969, and it was agreed with the paper's accounts department that I should first spend up to three days, with travelling expenses, near the scene of the crime. The obvious place to stay was Wissant, where I booked in at the Hotel de la Plage. A waiter at the hotel found me a driver, a pleasant young man by the name of Yves Richard.

Trials, even in French courts, are rarely very amusing. The case itself was interesting, if only because of the nature of part of the evidence for the prosecution, which consisted of a tape recording made by an Iranian Kurd who had served in the Foreign Legion and had somehow ended up in Peuplingues. He had died early that year, so that he would not be able to be cross-examined about the recording and so, of course, that, in swanning about the neighbourhood, we journalists would not have been able to interview him. We could simply peer in at the windows of his hovel, under the discouraging gaze of a member of the local *gendarmerie*. The recording itself was of a conversation between *le Kurd* (alternatively known as *le Turc*, which is not quite so foolish as it might at first seem, since many Kurds are Turkish citizens, Kurdistan having no political existence) and M. Rohart, from which it appeared that the latter was urging the former to help him devise means of murdering his wife.

We all listened to this in the oddly frivolous-looking courtroom at St Omer, with its florid nylon wallpaper and net curtains, the presiding judge having warned the jury that they must not attach undue weight to it as evidence. More important, since Rohart claimed that Mme Rohart had died by drowning, was the fact that the forensic laboratory had found no sea water in her lungs, but had found traces of barbiturate in her stomach. He was found guilty and sentenced to life imprisonment.

The trial had lasted only four days, despite the crowd of witnesses heard. I returned to Wissant and to the Plage, with which I had been very well satisfied.

I wanted to stay at some such watering place (as we used so quaintly to call them) for a rest, after the death of my wife, which had left me disinclined to social life, especially in London. Yves Richard had an elder brother, Jean-Paul, who was a fisherman. I spent a day or two out with him in his boat, and we hit it off very nicely. I sent him a Christmas card.

The St Omer verdict was quashed on a technicality, and the case of Armand Rohart came on again at Douai the following year, in April. Having covered the first trial so comprehensively, *The Examiner* felt it should also cover the second. I went to Douai. The verdict and the sentence were the same.

Wissant is fifty miles from Douai, but I went there again and booked in at the Plage. I was smiled on by the management and the waiters. By Jean-Paul Richard I was greeted as an old friend, and we spent a very pleasant week fishing in unsettled weather.

Nine years passed. I sent Jean-Paul nine Christmas cards.

I CROSS QUEEN'S Parade. Passing the broad side (where there were some broken windows) and big car-park (in which anybody may now park whatever he pleases) of the Metropole hotel, I am in Castle Road. Across it is the castle.

On this side, my left, after the Metropole hotel car-park, comes the first of eleven tall, inelegant houses, in the last but three of which Porteous, the dentist, practises. The house is overgrown with Virginia creeper. Its front room on the ground floor is his waiting-room, and through its bay window, from nine o'clock onward, will be seen a group of four or five people who sit with folded arms, awaiting torture. Castle Road takes me a hundred and eighty paces. I come to Jubilee Road and, before I cross it, look with particular interest at the two houses slightly to the right on the other side, whose curtains, I am relieved to see, are still drawn.

Clarendon House, on the corner, has only one upper floor. It is a pretty house, and Sidney Colvin, who has lived

12

there with his wife for just over two years, had it painted a nice pink. The house to its right is unpainted. This house belongs to those, eight of them including a baby, who at the back have been our immediate neighbours for just over three years. It is taller, but not so tall as the row of four houses which come next.

The gardens of the first two of these are mere stretches of weedy gravel, on the first of which cars are parked. I cross Jubilee Road and see that the unpainted house has a garden which receives expert attention every now and then, but is at the moment full of weeds.

The Colvins' garden is smaller by reason of the fact that its corner has been cut away and a municipal bench placed there. Whereas the other gardens are unfenced or have railings in bad repair, the Colvins' is enclosed on two sides by white palings with rounded tops. The surface of their garden was, by a previous occupant, roughly cemented over in such a way as to leave numerous small patches of soil, in which Julia has planted a great variety of flowers, some of them unknown by name to me, one kind to each patch. The effect was pleasing in the extreme, and even now there is much on show.

Negotiating the crossroads, I am in Clarendon Road. Once I am in Clarendon Road I must walk forty-five paces to reach a road sign, still illuminated as it has been all night. Half-way to the sign, I pass what must be regarded as the front door of Clarendon House, since it faces Jubilee Road, but stands at the top of seven steps which are undoubtedly in Clarendon Road and thus at the far side of the house.

From the sign, five or six more paces bring me to our wrought-iron gate. The gate is no more than two or three feet broad and in height somewhat shorter than myself, except for the twin curlicues in the middle, which rise to little under six feet. A peculiarity to be noted here is that the gate swings from brickwork, itself a little shorter than myself, of which two or three feet to either side connect its

13

hinges and catch with pillars more than six feet high. These are three yards apart, and there is a gap of three yards in the kerb of the pavement, which at this point slopes down to the roadway as a mere ramp, from which it might be deduced that a wider gate formerly opened here and that fairly heavy vehicles drove in and out. The shorter brickwork is more recent than that of the pillars.

Even if the gateway were restored to its old breadth, no vehicle could now nose in more than a yard or so, because at that distance, through the wrought-iron gate, may be seen a bow window composed of sixty rectangular panes of glass, backed with nylon net, behind the outer twenty panes old-gold curtains being further visible. On a narrow piece of off-white wall directly facing the centre of the window may be indistinctly seen what I know to be a lithograph by Henry Moore, before it a square table of dark oak. To either side of the narrow piece of wall are doors, both closed, both painted cream.

Opening the wrought-iron gate, passing through and closing the gate carefully behind me, for it has no spring and the catch must be lifted and dropped into place, I turn left and take four or five paces to confront the house door, which I open first with a Chubb and then with a Sidleen latch key. At the house door, I am invisible from the street by reason of a six-foot wall. This wall is painted white, as are the walls of the house, with a narrow strip of black bitumen paint at the bottom. The window frames are white. The door is a deep blue-green, called ocean blue. So are the gutters, the framework below the gutters and the one drainpipe on this side of the house. The wrought-iron gate is painted black, and so is an old pump against the wall behind me. This painting was done almost exactly a year ago. That of the wall behind me was made more difficult by the growth in front of it of forsythia and variegated ivy.

I cross the threshold and am immediately on carpet of a colour for which the weavers' name is silver birch. It is a

14

kind of sage-green. Two yards to my left begin stairs similarly carpeted, and two feet to my right is a cream-painted door, through which, when I have shut the house door, I pass into our front room, already dimly seen through the bow window, first propping my stick in a corner of the hallway. Looking out through the bow window and the wrought-iron gate, I see our lower brickwork, the beginnings of the two pillars and anyone passing in Clarendon Road, whether pedestrians on the near or farther pavement or motorists in the roadway. For net curtaining over windows does not much obscure the view from inside a house.

This room is also carpeted silver birch, as, it would be found, is every floor throughout the house, except those of the kitchen, what we call the crime room and a bit of the conservatory. Our ground floor is not quite laid on what we nowadays call open plan, but there is no door, only an arch, between the front and back rooms. The doorway through which I entered this room is left open except in the very coldest weather or when, as has happened only twice in four years, we go away. I am tempted to prop it open now with the piece of white-flecked black pebble we keep there for the purpose, but I might leave it so propped, and that would be a mistake because of Julia Colvin and, indeed, because, when we return together, Alison might remember that we had shut that door when we left (but then would attribute its opening to Julia). There are, as I said, doors to either side of the narrow piece of wall directly facing the bow window, a sliding door to the small kitchen and a door on hinges to the lobby in which stands the water and central-heating boiler, while off this lobby a further door leads to the cloakroom.

FOR THE MOMENT, I put my plastic shopping-bag, which bears the name of the Galeries Wissantaises, on the stainless-steel trolley in the corner by the kitchen door. Having removed my Burberry, I dump it in the rocking-chair. I then go into the cloakroom, where Alison did leave a towel. I switch on the water heater.

From the plastic bag I take my vacuum flask and the parcel of English-type sandwiches, the crusts of which have been cut off. The first I eat of the sandwiches contains a very nice *pâté de Campagne*. The coffee is still pretty warm and has not formed a skin. I eat and drink at the square table of dark oak, beneath the lithograph by Henry Moore. I screw the cup back on the vacuum flask, fold the sandwiches which remain, with the fruit, into as neat a parcel as I can make and put both flask and parcel back into the plastic bag, where still lies another parcel, containing hardware.

I feel safe in this front room for the next hour and a half of what is bound to be a long and dreary day, spent on tenterhooks and without much in the way of animal comfort. The unknown or, indeed, all but a very few known people who pass our wrought-iron gate may look in, but from outside you cannot see much inside through the net curtains. Even if they saw me moving about, it would mean nothing, either then or later, to more than at most ten people, few of whom are likely to pass or to look in if they did or seriously to wonder afterwards how I had come to be there that morning. As to the others, they would have no reason to wonder.

I move about now. The postman has just put something through the letterbox. As usual, he has left the gate ajar. I make so bold as to open the house door, step out, turn left, take four indignant paces and close the wrought-iron gate, after which, about-turning, I take five paces back to the door.

Among the letters there is nothing that looks at all interesting either for my sister or myself. I leave the bills and circulars on the doormat, for Julia Colvin to find next time she looks in. Among the letters she has carefully stacked on the stripped-pine mantelpiece in the back room, one or two look as though they might be of some interest, but I must not open them now. I am careful to leave them in the same order on the same bit of the ledge.

I can see no pale-blue car in the carport at the far end of the next-door garden. This means that Fagg drove off at a quarter to six on an early shift and will arrive home in the early afternoon. Thereafter, he will go out again on his second job.

I am in the hall, where three paces take me to the foot of the first three steps. Up these, I turn left on a small landing with a step of its own and, turning left again round a square newel post, am on the first of a flight of ten steps, with a small window on my right and, on my left, a square banister rail, behind which, at a height most conveniently accessible to me when I am standing on the fourth of the ten steps, lies a fairly broad ledge on which I keep a number of large books and box-files. From among these I extract desk diaries for the last four years. I take them downstairs, place the three later ones on the table in the back room and retire with the earliest to a big, low-built, almost excessively comfortable chair in the far corner of the front room, from which, through the bow window, I could see anyone pass or improbably enter by the wrought-iron gate, but in which I am confident that nobody but the most practised looker-in would see me, except perhaps on an afternoon of bright sunlight, which we are unlikely to have today.

2: First Year

IT IS OVER four years since Alison and I first saw this house. My desk diary for the year (its cover dark blue) shows me that it was on April 25th, 1975, a Friday. A Mr Beckford, of Beckford & Beckford, left his office and himself came with us along Jubilee Road. At a point at which, to our right, a castle in good repair became visible and was, indeed, close, we took the first turning on the left, which was Clarendon Road, and crossed. As we crossed at an angle, twenty yards then brought us to a wrought-iron gate, behind which lay quite an impressive bow window.

The proximity of a castle apart, two points in this house's favour were thus quickly established. From outside, it had a superior, enclosed look. And it was not far from the shops, a point of more importance to my sister than to me. There seemed not to be much traffic in Clarendon Road, which had a slight downward slope, unusual in streets so near the sea.

The woman who let us in was the owner's nurse-companion, Mrs Nicholson. Mrs Fleming was a cripple. That was her only reason for wishing to sell the house. She could no longer get upstairs and was proposing to go and live in a ground-floor flat on the sea front. She sat upright, quite a handsome, well-preserved woman in her seventies, on a chair in the bow window. She addressed Mr Beckford as David, he her as Ethel.

The furniture in that room was pleasing, largely antique. The room through a narrow arch was largely occupied by

18

Mrs Fleming's bed, but it further contained a small, antique desk, a chair partly blocking the archway and an ornamental fireplace composed of pink-grained marble from the old Stock Exchange in London, surrounded and narrowly mantelled by machine-carved stripped pine. It was a garden room, in that from it one saw through the small conservatory to a garden much concreted, though a bit too large to be regarded as a mere *patio* in the contemporary English sense of that word.

Off the conservatory was a small room used as a boxroom and containing a huge wardrobe. Also on the ground floor were the kitchen, which I feared Alison might find too small, a lobby in which the central-heating boiler stood and a cloakroom. There were two bedrooms and a bathroom upstairs. These amenities we were shown by Mrs Nicholson.

Our second visit was on May 27th, the day after the spring bank holiday which has taken the place of Whit Monday. Angus Black, my son-in-law, was here. With my daughter, Erica Jo, and their children, he had been spending the weekend at a house they have inland. He met us at the railway station here as we arrived from London. Negotiations for the purchase of this house had by then been completed subject to survey, and Angus was here to conduct, as he is competent to do, whatever survey he felt was desirable.

The five years during which my sister had still been allowed to fill temporary posts under the Inner London Education Authority would be up on the 18th of July, her seventieth birthday, a convenient date, since it was the end of the school term and, indeed, the school year. On that date, Alison Frobisher, *née* Atha, was finally superannuated by the ILEA.

My sister and I having decided to live thereafter chastely together here, we took possession of this house on July 19th, a Saturday. The gas stove was delivered that morning, and to take delivery of this was all that seemed possible that day. We slept that night and were to sleep seven more nights at the Blacks' holiday home, to within half a mile of which buses luckily ran from North Street, which branches off to the sea front from the point at which Jubilee Road becomes High Street and begins with a shopping precinct.

Much of the following week was spent in buying and adjusting curtains, for which adequate fittings were already in place. On Wednesday, a gasman came and connected the stove. From the firm of Hopkins & Wheeler, which no longer exists, Mr Wheeler himself also came that day and started putting up bookshelves on the frontmost wall of our front room, the wall beyond which lies what since May of the year before last has been the Colvins' passage.

Our furniture, some of Alison's but more of mine, arrived from London on Friday, the 25th, seen off by my excellent son-in-law. The new bookshelves were already in place, the paint still a bit tacky. By early evening our furniture, including various sets of other bookshelves, was in the rooms it should be in, books stacked everywhere, glass and china still in tea chests. Apart from spreading a small rug on the Marley tiles of the little room off the conservatory, formerly a boxroom but to become known as the crime room, mainly because of the books which would be concentrated in the large bookcase there (it also contained a narrow divan bed), there was nothing to do about the floors, the sage-green or silver birch carpeting having been bought with the house. The kitchen had undistinguished linoleum rather poorly laid. The conservatory also had Marley tiles, dark brown in colour.

We were still sleeping that night and the next at Erica Jo's, but the following night slept here. That Sunday was my sixty-fourth birthday.

I slept in the smaller bedroom, which has only one window, facing north, whereas Alison's room has one facing north and another facing west, overlooking the

20

garden. By way of further orientation, I may say that my bedroom and the bathroom are at the easternmost end of the house, over the front room downstairs and adjacent to Clarendon House or, rather, its passage. It is the end towards Jubilee and, more remotely, Castle Road and the sea front. The bathroom window and that of a landing outside the bathroom door overlook Clarendon Road, facing south. I am thus, to a limited extent, insulated from night noise in Clarendon Road.

That year, I was to spend a hundred and fifty-eight nights in the same bedroom. As one year was a leap year, it would have an extra night. By September 3rd, I had this year spent two hundred and forty-one of the year's first two hundred and fifty-two nights here. Altogether, therefore, I had then slept one thousand, four hundred and ninety-five nights in the same room, the first three hundred and ten of them with a fair contentment.

THE ENTRIES IN this first of the five relevant diaries are short and sometimes no longer legible even to me. The one subject on which it might be consistently helpful is the weather, for I hardly ever missed noting that. Thus, on the first Monday morning, that of our first full day here, I note that mist blew inland and that a foghorn boomed from somewhere out at sea.

The day brightened and grew hot. In the evening, Alison and I decided to try the bar at the Metropole hotel, on our nearest bit of sea front. It was a nice bar, with a view out to sea, but for two gin-and-tonics, that is to say, two single measures of gin and one baby tonic, we were charged 82 pence, whereas two gin-and-tonics elsewhere in 1975 would cost between 54 and 58 pence, wherefore we decided that the Metropole hotel bar was a clip joint and that we would not go there again.

For this reason, if for no other, the Metropole hotel will not enter much into my story, except as a point of

21

topographical reference. As that, it seems likely to assume a certain importance.

We retraced our steps and came again to Jubilee Road, crossed it and continued down Clarendon Road. We passed our wrought-iron gate and came to Fontenoy Road, where we turned right and also tried the George. There, I drank a half-pint of draft bitter, which gave me indigestion. I doubted whether I should go there again. On our way home, we turned down or, I suppose, very slightly up some other street and then right into Clarendon Road by our back wall, along Hassell Lane.

In those days, I did not walk with a stick. Nor did I often count paces, which I assumed to be each a yard long, whereas now they average thirty inches, as I established some weeks ago by taking two repeatedly along a tape measure stretched out on the carpet in our back room. Thus I have said that the length of Castle Road was a hundred and eighty paces. It would then have been a hundred and fifty yards.

We had walked once each way along Castle Road that evening. It was no hardship. Neither had I then taken the least interest in the whereabouts of the house in which Porteous, the dentist, practised from nine o'clock in the morning until five or six in the evening, with a break of uncertain duration at lunchtime.

That evening must have been warm. Two days later, though I dare say it was a bit lower here, the temperature had reached 88 degrees Fahrenheit in London and elsewhere. The following Monday was the hottest day since 1948. A temperature of 93 degrees was recorded in parts of Kent.

It was the Monday after that when my sister and I rounded the corner, walked forty or fifty yards to the left and crossed what was still Jubilee Road, further crossed the pavement on the far side, were then on the broad, cobbled bridge over the castle moat and came to a massive, nail-studded door. Once inside, we paid our entrance fees,

Alison's smaller than mine because she was already a senior citizen, at a desk which also sold postcards and guides, and proceeded to look round the castle. We seemed to be the only customers.

I had toyed with the notion that a habit I might adopt was that of regularly standing on top of the keep at sunset, meditating perhaps and eventually writing a novel or real-life book about some dark deed which had been perpetrated or great love pursued in the castle since it was built in the reign, so the printed guide told me, of Henry VIII. But it seemed never to have been the scene of any famous love or murder or, so far as I could gather, of anything much except a bit of fighting between cavaliers and roundheads. I also found that you cannot climb up and stand on top of the keep, despite the lack of residential quarters within. You can go no higher than the battlements of the outer bastions, and you would have to leave these at sundown. The sun, in any case, goes down not over the sea but directly inland, among houses. It is true that full moons must therefore rise over the sea, but those you cannot ordinarily observe, since the castle is closed at the time of their rising.

The castle is in excellent condition, and an architect might find much there to interest him. Although a direct hit by a German bomb destroyed its residential quarters during the war of forty years ago, it must contain at least an office, which the captain sometimes uses, his very odd flag flying over the keep when he is on the premises and thus, however briefly, "in residence". The present captain is knighted and looks a very nice man. I have never met him. Alison has.

At the time of our first visit to the castle, we had no net over the bow window. It was in fact to be almost two years before we reluctantly had net put up. Its lack exposed us to the gaze of passers-by, who looked straight through the wrought-iron gate and window to the Henry Moore lithograph, the square table in front of this, the kitchen

23

door and, as often as not, the kitchen itself, with in it a window through which they could further see into the next-door garden. People did look in, especially women. Occasionally, a group would stand at the gate and really study the house or at least a part of the front room.

That first August, we had no means of knowing whether the glancers and starers were local people or summer visitors. We hoped they might be the latter, though we had found that this town housed, on the whole, a good class of summer visitor, doubtless because its steep shingle did not make an ideal beach for children.

In the morning of the last day of August, a Saturday, a tired-looking woman, carrying what might have been a bag of laundry, stood at the gate and looked in for some minutes. I was outside the house door in the narrow space within the six-foot street wall. I went to the gate.

"Can I help you?" said I, ready to follow with some rather tart remark.

"No, you can't help *me*," said the woman. "I was just being rude and staring. It's such a pretty place, a pretty window."

I HAD NEVER before had a garden of my own, and the only gardening implements here when we arrived, left by Mrs Fleming, were a rake and a garden fork. To these a spade and a handfork were quickly added by my daughter, who also bought me, as a birthday present, an incinerator of the dustbin type. By purchase at various times and from various places I further acquired a trowel, a pair of sécateurs, a pruning saw, a riddle, an *Everyman's Encyclopaedia of Gardening*, a heavy pair of long shears (paid for with my sister's Green Shield stamps) and a compost bin.

I was somewhat inhibited by the knowledge, from Mrs Nicholson's and David Beckford's information, that bulbs lay widely distributed in the soil. Exactly where, I should not know until it was spring. It was not digging them up that I feared, for the time of year was all right for putting them back, but that my spade, fork or trowel would damage them, impaling them or slicing them in two. So I did little digging, except here and there, where I fancied there would not be bulbs, and even so managed to impale or slice a fair number.

The only things I put into the ground that autumn were two or three dozen wallflower plants. It seemed wiser to confine myself to what may be called destructive gardening, which is indeed a kind recommended for autumn.

Against the six-foot wall outside our front (really, side) door, the variegated ivy and forsythia grew from a single small rectangle of soil set in the pebbled concrete. They were hopelessly intertwined in their upper reaches, their stems, two or three inches thick, so closely packed together, ivy alternating with forsythia, that it would have been impossible to dig any of them up by the roots or even to cut many of them down to near ground level.

I had to decide to which side the forsythia should be encouraged to grow and to which side the ivy. I decided that the forsythia could grow to the right (as seen from the door) and that the ivy should be as nearly as possible confined to the pillar which terminated the six-foot wall on the door side of the wrought-iron gate. This involved, first, a great deal of sécateur work and then much use of the pruning saw close to the wall. The product was a great deal of bonfire material, which I placed on the concrete outside the conservatory doors, sawing up the heavier branches and putting as much as I could of the upper ivy in a large cardboard box, which I hoped the dustmen would remove (they did) when they emptied the dustbin on Wednesday morning. This was not to be the only bonfire material.

Four or five paces to the right of what I shall continue to call our front door is a gate, between pieces of wall, which connect the house with the street wall. This gate is kept bolted on the garden side and can therefore only be passed through if one goes out of the conservatory door and unbolts it. It is a flimsy gate. It occurs at the point at which the house ended before the conservatory and the small room off it were added.

I do not propose to pass through this gate at the moment, if indeed I do so at all today. I do not wish, more than is strictly necessary, to risk being seen by Mrs James from any of the bedroom windows in her guest house across Hassell Lane. But I may, I think, claim to know, none better, that, once on the other side of the gate, we should have on our left the continuation of the street wall and, in front of it, something of a rockery, from which rise two lilac trees. At first, before them, came a holly tree. This put out small blossoms, which, I saw from an illustration in *Everyman's Encyclopaedia of Gardening*, were male blossoms. The tree would therefore never bear berries. I decided to cut it down.

To cut it down, with my small pruning saw, would be a long job, after which there would be the slow killing of the stump with a substance called SBK. But I sawed the branches off and cut them up, and that made a lot of further bonfire material. There were, in addition, the prunings of various trees and shrubs, some of which were mere jobs for the sécateurs, but others of which required the saw. And so I was able to satisfy my pyromania very thoroughly that autumn.

THE PAVILION IS to the south of the pier. It is mainly a dance hall, but also houses flower shows, political meetings and musical performances.

The low ceiling of varnished wood is surrounded, at a higher level, by glass, upon which the rain may noisily beat when it is raining outside, but the acoustics of the hall is not the only trouble at the Pavilion. The seating also leaves much to be desired, since it consists of tubular chairs covered with orange-coloured canvas, inadequately numbered, so that arguments break out as to whose seat this or that is. The chairs slither about on a floor intended,

26

in the first place, for dancing. On the other hand, a good bar opens when a concert (or, presumably, a dance) is afoot, and the floral decoration in the large, carpeted foyer is on occasion superb. From outside, the building is architecturally unexceptionable.

The finest building in the town is the naval hospital, which is at the northern end of the town and has been there since Nelson's time. It is topped by a handsome cupola, with a clock in its base and above it a weathervane. We hear the clock strike the hour and chime the quarters, at any rate when the wind is in the north (it is in the west now, which is why I was so little conscious of it as I came along the sea front). Like the castle, the cupola is floodlit at night. Its colour in daylight is a pale grey.

MY DESK DIARY for that year is bound in dark blue, that for the following year in bright red. They being there at the time, for part of their children's school holidays, it appears that Alison and I went to Erica Jo's and Angus's holiday home inland (some five miles inland) on the very first day of the following year. This must have been the day on which, while there, I drove the gardener's spade with great force into a bush, which I meant to split and so secured cuttings. The spade met solid wood and gave my right arm a terrible jolt.

My arm was suffering somewhat already from the effects of sécateur work and sawing. It was three weeks before the pain became acute. I lay awake with the pain in my arm during a night when I also wheezed horribly. Next morning, I went to doctors next door but two around the corner, one of whom my sister had already seen and with whom we had registered. I asked for him. He was Dr Roper. He had a fair beard and shaved his top lip. His appearance was more youthful than he can possibly be, since he has four sons.

Antibiotics were prescribed for the wheezing, Distalgesic and a drug whose name I couldn't read for my arm. I

27

hadn't till then seen a doctor for almost nine years, not in fact since, by an unpleasant business with enemas of barium and subsequent X-raying, I had been discovered to have diverticulitis. My aching arm might, it was thought, be an extension of the osteo-arthritis which had been diagnosed in my legs and especially my right knee almost fifteen years before.

On the last day of the month, there was an admirable song recital at the Pavilion by Ian and Jennifer Partridge. The piano was adequate for accompanying songs, and, as he was standing towards the front of the platform, Ian Partridge's voice was untroubled by the acoustics of the place.

In February, there were snowdrops, but no Dutch crocuses followed. It was on the 20th that, in the evening, Erica Jo, Angus and their children drove down to the holiday home for a single night and that, as though they had cleverly forecast it, the next day was one of those perfect days of early spring of which there always seems to be one in February, after which it will turn colder and dull again. In the morning, Angus drove us round to look at churches. Three crocuses, delicately mauve, of the kind known as botanical, were suddenly open when we got back here for lunch.

Early March was very cold indeed. There was a pair of redwings in the garden. There were redwings all over England that year. It had something to do with the weather. The first daffodils were out on the 29th. One or two hyacinths had beaten them to it. With the spring bulbs up, I was able to plant and sow a great deal, including culinary and salad herbs, in which I intended to specialise. In the conservatory, in plant pots and in soil which I had boiled, I sowed seeds of *mimosa pudica*, the sensitive plant, which was to afford great amusement to Erica Jo's children.

At the beginning of April, the garden next door and its house were still empty. As we understood, the doctors, next beyond, had been thinking of buying that house to

28

extend their premises, but had been told that it needed eight thousand pounds spending on it. We hadn't seen anyone looking round lately.

Clarendon House also, at the corner, was empty and was to remain empty for another year. We had paid very little attention to either emptiness. We supposed that sometime the houses would be full. We imagined that it might add to the interest of our lives.

On the 13th of April, there was blossom on a big cherry tree which stood on the north side of our garden, the side away from Clarendon Road, where a concrete path runs along the side of the house past the kitchen window. On the 14th, there was a profile of the famous author, Harold Atha, in the local paper, with a photograph of me at my typewriter.

Easter Sunday was the 18th. As is customary, the gardens of great houses were open to the public for charity. Angus, down again at his house inland, took us to one which had some connection with Jane Austen. The owner's wife told us that something had been staged there at the time of her bicentenary.

When Alison came back from her shopping on the 21st, she said that the house next door at the back had a SOLD notice at the front. We wondered what sort of neighbours we should get. Of course, if eight thousand pounds were to be spent on the house first, they would probably not be moving in quite yet.

That was to be the year of the great drought. It had already been proclaimed, which meant that the previous autumn had contributed to it. By April 29th, it had reached a point at which our rainwater butt (really a dustbin painted black) was all but empty. I turned it upside down to get rid of black mud, rust and newspaper in the bottom, then stood it in the sun to air and dry. This receptacle normally stands in the corner opposite the cherry tree, outside an open shed which (with a closed one) drains into it, near the substantial back gate opening on to Hassell

Lane, but its two bolts as a rule unfastened only on Wednesday mornings for the dustmen.

THE PERSONS OF three generations in the next garden on the evening of May 3rd were presumably our future neighbours. They looked what I suppose would be called respectable working-class and were rather numerous, but would no doubt not all be living in the house. They would include either the parents of a family that was coming to live there or the children and grandchildren of an older couple who were. Artlessly, I should have supposed that they would not have the eight thousand pounds that needed spending on the house, as well as its purchase price of, I understood, eleven thousand.

They appeared again the next evening, and I was surprised by how closely they seemed to pass by our kitchen window on their way from the garden to the house. I could see that it was only a yard or so from the wall of the house to the garden wall and that their concrete path ran immediately on the other side of the garden wall, which was low outside the kitchen window or would have blocked it. I supposed that, when people were looking round before, I had not seen them from this angle, in our front room, with the sliding kitchen door open.

I heard only a rumble of voices, with no words distinctly heard. I seemed, nevertheless, to detect a north-country intonation in the speech of the taller, older man with spectacles and the woman with a sort of brown, woolly tea-cosy on her head.

3: Neighbours

WE HAD BEEN there for almost ten months and had made a fair number of friends and acquaintances in the town, many as a result of Alison's encounters while out shopping or at the music and history societies, which she had joined early on. The secretary of the latter had once been a BBC secretary and remembered me from a broadcast I had once done (I did not, I fear, remember her). My sister's closest friend was probably the Mrs Nicholson whom we had first met as Ethel Fleming's nurse-companion here, though she had a house of her own in this town's residential suburb. The two regularly met, with others, to drink coffee in the morning at a place I did not know, called the Parlour, apparently on the sea front.

May 6th was sunny, and a car-owning friend, here to lunch, thought it would be nice for Alison and me to be driven to a beach some distance away. My sister was stung on the neck by a wasp. The place became red and painful, though without much swelling. It was treated, on our return home, with vinegar, wasps' stings being said to be alkaline, unlike those of bees, which are acid and require bicarbonate of soda.

That had been quite a hot day. The next day, Friday, was the hottest May day for twenty-four years, with a temperature of 82 degrees recorded in London. So we read in the *Daily Mail* the following morning.

That weekend, the older man came to the house on both days, accompanied by the woman in the tea-cosy hat (who only watched), and, despite the heat, performed a very strenuous kind of destructive gardening, for which it was not at all the time of year. He chopped down and grubbed up an apple tree, one of two, in the next-door garden and a forsythia which grew out of a (presumed, for I could not see it) patch of soil in an area of concrete raised up two steps outside their back doors.

He also, with a sickle, slashed down a border of flowering plants which grew against the far wall of the garden, its southward-facing wall, across the overgrown grass, and which must have been almost on the point of flowering. This suggested that he did not like flowers. Except for the lupins, whose foliage is unmistakable, he can hardly have known what sort of flowers they all were. I knew, from the year before, that some of them were beautiful and interesting. I had more than once thought of nipping over the wall, while the house was empty, and digging them up. I should probably have done this, had it not been for how clearly visible that garden was from the upstairs window of Mrs James's guest-house across Hassell Lane. I could, in any case, have done it with the agent's permission, since David Beckford, who had become a friend of ours, was co-agent at that time.

I can't think why exactly I had objected to Mrs James seeing me in the next garden digging up plants. I was perhaps excessively law-abiding and hated to think that she might suppose me careless of the *convenances* of neighbourly life, even when there were no neighbours. Certainly, she would not have reported me. We liked Mrs James.

I HAD COME to Sunday, May 9th. Monday was a bit cooler and started misty, with the foghorn booming. On Tuesday, a wind arose, and the evening was cloudy.

On Wednesday, there was rain in the morning. In the evening, however, the older man transferred his attention to the front garden in Jubilee Road and uprooted a hedge of cotoneaster on his side of the very low wall which separated that garden from the shorter garden of Clarendon House. *Cotoneaster horizontalis* is not, to my mind, a suitable plant for hedges, and I could well have understood him uprooting this one if he had thereafter planted another hedge of something more suitable, but this he has never done. I did not see him uprooting the cotoneasters, but I saw various children dragging them down Clarendon Road, with many a smiling or, as I should have said, grinning glance in at our bow window, over which we then had no net. One cannot see children or any but tall adults pass along even the short stretch of our part of Hassell Lane where the Montana clematis does not grow over wicker fencing, but drag the cotoneasters along there is presumably what they did and then dumped them in the next-door back garden.

The following weekend, a short, thickset young man with fair, wavy hair was demolishing a brick shed in the far corner of this garden. A load of sand had been deposited on the raised concrete yard, together with bags of cement. From time to time, the younger man left his demolition to join with the older in mixing sand and cement with water, the resulting mixture being taken by the older man in buckets into the house. It began to look as though the two were proposing to do the eight thousand pounds' worth of work on the house themselves and both live in it, with their women and children. Having finished demolishing the shed, the younger, fair-haired, stocky man started to demolish the street wall on to Hassell Lane.

On Tuesday, the 18th of May, there was drizzling rain. Wednesday was cloudy, with a chilling wind. Alison nevertheless put us up some sandwiches, and I was driven off to the county town to watch the West Indies play the county at cricket. The West Indies had gone in to bat. Under that dull sky and in that wind, I found it difficult to feel much interest in the game.

By Friday, the wall on to Hassell Lane, apart from a gate

33

adjoining ours, was more than half down, and the broken bricks, from shed and wall, had been stacked along the concrete path beyond our garden wall, overtopping it in height. Through the gap, at eight o'clock that evening, was driven, by the older man, a large white van labelled INVICTA VAN HIRE. Immediately, people, including children, poured out of the house and began moving furniture and boxes from the van to the house.

The van spent that night and the following two nights in the garden, departing in the daytime to bring further loads. Apart from what was taken into the house, things from the van were dumped in the garden. Among these were four bicyles and a tricycle, two wheelbarrows, a hundred or more large plant pots and cylindrical concrete shapes, a number of watering cans, buckets and chipped enamel bowls, what I took to be a disused bathroom tank or cistern, the sections of a large greenhouse and a curious little hut, something between a bathing hut and a ticket office.

That Monday morning, in the course of her shopping, my sister called in at the area office, which is the southernmost building in Alexandra Road, all past there being High Street. She wanted to know what planning permission our future neighbours had. To date, they had none.

The woman to whom Alison spoke said: "What *is* going on there? Dr Millard has already been in to enquire."

Dr Millard was not one of the consortium who practised in the next house along. She was an elderly woman, with a bad limp and a yet older sister. They lived in the house beyond the consortium of doctors. Dr Millard had retired from general practice, but still did two clinics a week at a hospital in the nearest big seaport.

On Wednesday evening, I answered the doorbell to a man whom I recognised as the older of the two men whom I had seen in the next garden, a man, I fancied, in his early sixties, very active in a jerky sort of way, somewhat

34

bowlegged, quite tall and with a bit of a stoop, bespectacled, sallow-complexioned, grey and almost bald. That evening, he was rather smartly dressed and wore a hat.

I had not been wrong about the north-country intonation, and I imagined that he and his wife came from the West Riding, as I did, though, to the best of my knowledge, I had in forty years lost all traces of accent. So far as I had gathered, the younger members of my caller's family all spoke with the kind of sub-Cockney which is prevalent in this neighbourhood, though with something a bit more local and even rural among the fishermen.

His manner was pleasant enough, even ingratiating. He wanted, he said, to put up a garage, but could not have planning permission before July. Area office had suggested to him that he should ask his nearest neighbours whether they had any objection. I had none, I said, to any reasonable sort of garage.

His name was Porringer, which I had never come across in Yorkshire. He and his were moving in on Friday. There were to be seven of them. Apart from Tea-Cosy, the others comprised a daughter and son-in-law, their two children (I thought he said) and (I also thought he said) his son-in-law's sister, who would be staying with them for a while. She no doubt was the heavily built teenager we called the Whistler, whom at first we had supposed to be a boy and who might be heard stumping up and down the concrete path just over our wall on stilts.

They moved in. My bedroom window overlooked their chaos. I was usually awake by five o'clock and up by six. Drawing back my curtains that Sunday morning, the 30th of May, I saw that a milkman had left, at their porch door, a crate designed for eight pint bottles, containing seven. A carton of cream or yoghourt stood beside it.

IT IS A QUARTER past eight. I have walked into the hallway, up three steps, on to a landing with a step in it

35

and, there turning twice to the left, round the square newel post, up ten more steps, with the ledge holding big books on my left, on to the landing outside Alison's bedroom, three yards forward, which take me to the bathroom door, and to the left into my bedroom, the floors all covered with silver-birch carpeting, the walls all off-white, the paint-work cream. I go forward to a point not too near my window.

My divan bed is behind me, covered with a somewhat ragged but heavy, woollen, green cover. On the walls are, to my left, over the walnut chest of drawers, a small, square, oak-framed mirror and the drawing of a street by a Sunday artist, a doctor, whose work Angus admires, to the right of the window a rather modernistic watercolour of what I take to be a wood nymph, her arms sprouting branches, her legs tree trunks, behind me a charcoal and sanguine drawing of a cat and the artist's girlfriend and on the low wall to my left (the white ceiling slopes over my bed) a microscopic Victorian coloured engraving of a local scene with a railway train. The walls to either side of the window are stained rather with condensation than with damp from outside. The curtains are of much the same deep green-blue as much of the paintwork outside the house has been for the past year. There is a Windsor chair in front of the bookshelves in the far left-hand corner.

As I finish this inventory, my patience is rewarded by the opening of the semi-opaque glass kitchen door and the clear glass porch door a little to the right below my window and the emergence of Porringer and the two girls, the one we still call the Whistler and Denise, both now three years older than when I first saw them, Denise perhaps fourteen, the Whistler sixteen. Grandad also is older. So am I.

It is a measure of the closeness of their path to our house that I cannot see the path itself without almost pushing my nose against the window and, from as near as I dare go at the moment, can barely see three heads passing below. They will go out into Hassell Lane through the white gate, turn right and again right into the carport, and presently Porringer's car will nose out from this into Hassell Lane, turning to the right.

While they are in the carport, I shall observe them only by colour and movement, the dark colour of the school uniforms (this being the first day of the autumn term), probably not Porringer's lighter clothes but for a moment his cloth cap and the colour of the car itself. This, a Triumph, I should for long have described simply as off-white, but it is in fact a very pale green. They will drive off to the nearby town, to two separate schools, the girls to a grammar school, he to the mere secondary where he teaches woodwork.

The reason why I see people and cars dimly in the carport is that it is made of moulded concrete shapes, each with five interstices and each the size of four bricks laid horizontally. There are ninety shapes, interspersed with brickwork pillars and with a brickwork section at the near end, in the two walls of the carport (for at the far side it joins the doctors' car-park wall), and Porringer made them himself, one at a time, each evening, with a single mould, next day storing the shapes in a basement room. He also made two kinds of parapet shapes, pyramids for the brickwork pillars and lengths of continuously pointed parapet for the rest, only three pyramids but twenty-two lengths of continuous parapet. It must therefore have taken him a hundred days or three months, ever since February, after which came a long and elaborate job of bricklaying, with frequent mixings of cement.

The porch was one of Porringer's earlier pieces of work and led to one of the only two exchanges of words that have passed between us in three years and four months. It is a splendid structure, comprehensively glazed, its woodwork painted white. It replaced a very poor thing indeed, which had been here in the time of the previous owner and remained for a considerable time after the arrival of the Porringers and Faggs, I shall know for exactly how long when I come to that diary. It was painted black. It had very little glass and a corrugated-iron roof.

In about twenty minutes, there will, or there should, emerge from the present porch Jeremy, the third and presumably last of the Lambert children, a boy of nine or ten who attends the local elementary school. I need to know that all three of the older children are out of the house, though Jeremy is not much given to looking up at this or in at the kitchen window.

While I wait for him, I shall dwell on the view from this window and the comparatively few changes which have taken place in it during four years. From here, I can see, of the Jameses' premises, only their garage. After this, on the far side of Hassell Lane, comes a passage, closed by a door (this was not always so) which leads to the backs of houses down Clarendon Road.

Then comes the drill hall. From here, on Monday evenings, air-force cadets may be heard drumming. Occasionally, a bugle may also be heard. In the upper rooms, the male cadets may afterwards be seen chasing the girls, who are better drummers and smarter on parade than most of the boys. The drill hall stands on a corner. Its entrance is in a road of which I can never remember the name.

The houses on our side of Hassell Lane, which has no pavement, are all, except ours, the backs of houses whose frontage is in the northern end of Jubilee Road. After that of our immediate neighbours stands a row of four tall houses, not, originally, without a certain elegance. Nobody lives in the first, third and fourth of these, though all four are much occupied in the daytime.

The first contains the surgeries, waiting-room, receptionists' office and radiologist's room of the doctors with whom my sister and I are registered. For a year and a half after our arrival, they had an unused back garden of overgrown grass, with one or more unpruned trees and a dilapidated shed. It is now an asphalted car-park.

Dr Millard's garage is bigger than she needs and unsightly, with a roof of corrugated iron. As much of her back garden as is not occupied by garage Dr Millard keeps pretty well, with the grass cut and the shrubs and flowers tended, but she had put up, on top of her garden wall, four pieces of the kind of fencing I have seen called golden larch, three of which have remained in place, but of which the fourth, oddly shaped because of an upward slope of the wall, has fallen cockeyed.

The two farthest from us of that row of four houses belong to the Ministry of Health & Social Security, which employs people to cut the grass. From the back of the nearer of its two houses (perhaps of the other one, too, but I cannot see it) juts an annexe on stilts which overlooks Dr Millard's garden oppressively, though it has the advantage of sheltering her from the north, with no loss of sun.

Dr Millard has two splendid rambler roses, one yellow, one a deep red, growing up against the stilts of the nearer Health & Social Security house. Her garden also contains a big, productive apple tree and a smaller tree which I believe to be hawthorn. Her house is painted white, with black drainpipes, the Health & Social Security houses a pale grey, with pale-green drainpipes, which are flaking badly. The Health & Social Security houses have had new windows since we came here. The frames of these are painted white. The back of the house in which the doctors practise is unpainted, like the house next door, though it is painted (pale grey) at the front, as theirs is not.

Follow the backs of a few smaller houses, which I cannot properly see from here. Beyond those rise the clock tower, cupola and weathervane of the naval hospital. . . . But here comes Jeremy. He is a well-built but nervy boy of nine or ten, a nuisance through circumstances beyond his control. I have often felt sympathetic towards him during the past summer, considering that his mother treats him unfairly, while Denise is sometimes positively brutal to him. He is

39

off to the local elementary school, from which he will return just before four o'clock.

That house was, I suppose, in Edwardian times, to somebody's commercial advantage, pushed in between Clarendon House and the row of four. Its garden walls have no buttresses, which means that the walls belong respectively to us and to the doctors. The date plaque in the wall on the doctors' side of the garden, being in their garden, they will think commemorates the erection of their house, but it will be the completion of the row of four to which it refers. The date is 1856, I seem to remember.

We have been unlucky to find so many of our smaller windows and those of the conservatory overlooking their garden. It might, in winter at least, have been worse if our house had directly adjoined theirs. That privilege is reserved to Clarendon House, whose coach-house we or part of us once were.

IT WAS FROM Dr Roper that we first had further information about our neighbours than our eyes and ears would provide us with. Dr Roper lives in a village to the south-west of this town, which for the moment keeps its separate name, but is administratively part of the town and uses its telephone exchange. It is an area of small bungalows, with one or two bigger houses and on its outskirts the beginning of fields. Dr Roper told my sister that our neighbours had lived in this village until recently, that the older man was a great gardener, noted for his blazes of colour, and that he taught at a school in the seaport to the north. He said that the younger man's name was Fagg and that he had worked on taxis, but was at present an instructor at a driving-school. This last piece of information I soon began to doubt.

The younger man's Christian name was Edward, as we presently discovered from hearing his wife call to him in the garden. When he had finished knocking down the wall on Hassell Lane and two cars were standing side by side at

40

the end of the garden, separated from the gatepost and the doctors' wall only by slender columns of ragged brick, it was to be seen that his, a small, dark-green one, bore an L-plate, but that might simply mean that he was teaching his wife to drive. He was to be heard driving off at a quarter to six in the morning, and that did not seem to me to be the time of day at which one would set off to take up one's duties at a driving-school. He was, moreover, to be seen around in the afternoon, when I should have thought a driving-school would begin to be busy.

There was nothing mysterious about the time that Porringer drove off in the morning. It would be towards half-past eight. This would get him to school nicely before nine o'clock. He always took with him, in the pale Triumph, the eldest of the three children, the Whistler, the one whom we supposed to be Fagg's sister and therefore the aunt of the other two, who we thought in fact called her Auntie. She would be wearing a summer school uniform of patterned, pale-blue effect. The two younger children were taken to school on foot by their mother and grandmother at about ten to nine and sometimes fetched at about ten to four in the afternoon by the two women, but sometimes by Fagg in his small, dark-green car.

When the senior Faggs were out, as they occasionally were, in the evening, Auntie would be put in charge of the two younger children, a boy we thought five or six, a girl we thought ten or eleven. The Whistler herself we thought to be thirteen or fourteen. She already had a pair of impressive breasts.

With the greater sophistication of a secondary-school girl, she would devise games for the others to play. There was hopscotch on the raised concrete. There were jumping games on the concrete path and a variety of ball games, in one of which the three took it in turns to sit on a pillar of jagged brick with a tennis racket and be fed with balls by the others in Hassell Lane. One evening, we even saw her sitting on the municipal bench at the Clarendon House corner and directing the two younger children in running to or from the island at the near-crossroads in Alexandra Road from or to the four nearby pavements in front of the cars which came at various speeds round two corners or along one straight road.

She herself was not an athletic girl, a bit fat, sluggish and inclined to walk with a waddle. She never stuck long at the jumping games, but left, for instance, the carefully devised high jump to the younger girl, who was better at it. On the other hand, she was quite good at sitting on the brick column by the gate and flicking away with a tennis racket, a game itself not without peril to the others, in view of the traffic which used Hassell Lane as a short cut.

This game, as may be imagined, was, since all three were right-handed, productive of balls in our garden. At first, we returned these, but presently took to putting them in the dustbin, to be removed by the dustmen on Wednesday mornings. It was a help in deciding to do this that, for a period in June, the balls were always in the garden when we returned from a visit to a public house or a walk along the sea front, so that, if the children had been round to our door to ask for their balls, they would have found us out.

They never seemed to call twice. The only child who called twice during this period was Mrs James's Marianne, whose manner was modest and charming, who was very pretty and, at that time, had long, dark hair. She got her ball back, a big, yellow one. At that time, she did not play with the Fagg children.

A puzzle presented itself when one of the balls which came over had the name "A. Lambert" written on it with a felt pen. It was a pale-green tennis ball of the kind which, I understand, is now used on hard courts. There had been several such balls over, as well as balls which had started their careers almost white and which are now confined to grass courts. We thought it one of the Whistler's balls, but it seemed unlikely that a ball belonging to Fagg's sister would have the name "A. Lambert" on it. It might, of

42

course, be a misappropriated ball or one taken by mistake in exchange for another.

One of the first things Porringer did about the house was to take down a clothes line left by the previous owner and substitute for it a blue plastic line, tied with a knot in the middle, which, being new and brightly coloured, was even more of an eyesore. Of the same type as the green line now over Dr Millard's garden, it extended, as the old one had done, from a pulley in the side of the porch to a rusty iron pole which thrust up among the branches of the remaining apple tree. This line hung close to our kitchen window, doubtless so that it could be reached from the concrete path. On it, the two women next door proceeded to hang clothes at a rate at which they could only have been turned out by a washing-machine. They began with a long row of knickers and underpants.

We thought it, indeed, understandable that, after moving house, they should be behind with the washing, but found, after some weeks, that the clothes line was still being filled three times a day. If we had left our kitchen door open, the washing was visible from Clarendon Road. This we did not like, if only because people passing would tend to assume that the washing was ours.

While the school term went on, it was only on Saturdays and Sundays that I heard Porringer hammering during the afternoon, when I wanted to sleep and had my bedroom window curtains drawn. He always did his hammering out of doors, on the raised concrete just under my bedroom window. It was there, too, that the children would be playing hopscotch or rumbling about on roller skates, having been turned out of the kitchen and dining-room towards two o'clock, after dinner, so that Mrs Porringer and Mrs Fagg and perhaps Fagg, after a brief rest, could clear away and wash up. A little later, they would be heard jumping or walking about on stilts on the concrete path lower down or shrieking as they threw balls to each other. Often enough, however, Fagg would, in those days, drive his family out for the day on either Saturday or Sunday, and then there would only be Grandad's hammering.

From hearing their mother call to them the length of the garden, we soon learned that the two younger children were Jeremy and Denise, genteel names used in full. In the early days, the parents sometimes practised other forms of genteel speech.

I once heard Mrs Fagg, coming up the garden path, say to the children, who had been kept indoors: "You may all have a bun."

It could even have been: "You may each have a bun."

I cannot remember what it was he was saying, but I also heard Fagg once, calling out from his car, pronounce an *h* where I should not have pronounced one, on the word "her". I was out in our garden on both occasions and imagine I was meant to hear these evidences of superior education.

Mrs Fagg always called her husband Edward, though no doubt he was Ted to his parents and siblings and any friends he might have. A schoolmaster's daughter might indeed have received some education, though I was soon to be convinced that what Porringer taught was wood-work.

4: A Slight Stroke

IT IS NOW safe for me to slide open the kitchen door, to put my remaining sandwiches on the refrigerator's red working top, the white-enamelled, metal draining-board or the white, L-shaped ledge which extends this on the left to a point just short of the gas stove, itself mostly white-enamelled, and to draw myself water, making fresh black coffee or tea (but I have no milk or lemon, and how should I get rid of tealeaves?), heating up the coffee in my vacuum flask or simply drinking water.

The kitchen is no more than two yards square, the area of absurdly mosaic-patterned, somewhat ill-fitted linoleum exposed and therefore able to be stepped on little more than a yard square, but it is well-fitted with cupboards, both at head height and beneath the sink and draining-board. It contains two windows, a small one at head height, of moulded glass, through which nothing but vague shapes can be seen and which does not open, and the window to the left which opens in an iron frame and consists of fifteen small, leaded panes. Over the equivalent of eight or nine of these (four completely covered, eight partly covered) I applied, some two years ago, a substance called Con-Tact, which has the effect of making clear glass appear frosted and frustrates the endeavours of people outside to look in (also, of course, of those inside to look out). To increase the amount of light admitted, I left the three top panes, the three half-panes immediately below them and the three bottom half-panes uncovered, these being positions at which our neighbours could not have looked in except by standing on something quite tall or by crouching down with their noses to the garden wall. In order that I might now and then keep my eye on them, I also left a panel uncovered down the side of two of the outer panes. They can, indeed, look in at the clear glass here, but would never see much, especially as the part-pane at head height is obscured by the iron fastening (which would, moreover, have made the Con-Tact difficult to apply at that point), while a small standard lamp on the tiled ledge largely blocks the part-pane below that.

The windows in the cloakroom and the lobby where the heater stands are of clear glass, but that in the cloakroom is above any but a very tall man's eye-level, and even that in the lobby is above the eye-level of either of the two women in the house or, I should think, Fagg's. It is true that any of these three might notice, through the kitchen window, not only me, if I was in their direct line of vision through the side panel, but, more generally, if increased light indicated that the kitchen door was open. But, whereas at one time the women were always out pegging up clothes, nowadays they almost never leave the back of the house by more than a few steps, at most once a day to put something in the dustbin by the gate. They are not, in any case, lookers-in (or lookers-over), whereas Fagg is. Him I shall have to play (as we say nowadays) "by ear" in his due time, which is not yet.

Not that, in any case, Mrs Fagg's seeing me would represent much danger, unless she were to say to Mrs Porringer or Fagg (both of whom I shall save if I can):

"I see Mr Atha's back."

It might not be "Mr Atha". It might be "the man next door". I fear, however, that they do know my name. I feel sure that they cannot know who or what I am. To them, we are simply a minor obstruction.

But I am not interested, at the moment, either in fresh black coffee or in water, and I do not much care to what

46

temperature the remains of my French *café au lait* have cooled. Besides, heating up coffee with the milk in tends to turn it a disagreeable colour. I unscrew the cup from the top of my vacuum flask, half-fill it with coffee, pour out the muddy remainder, rinse the flask, stand it upside down on the draining-board, take the cup into the front room, slide the kitchen door shut and return to my easy chair and my bright red desk diary for that year.

I hope that Julia Colvin will not look in this morning. If it were soon rather than at midday, she might well spot the vacuum flask even if I had got myself into the cloakroom, the crime room or upstairs, with my coat, my plastic bag, my walking-stick and my diaries.

THE WEATHER GREW hotter. By June 23rd, there were London temperatures of 88 degrees, by the 25th of 92 degrees, by the 26th of 95 degrees, an all-time record. And so, to the continuing drought, were added scorching suns.

Whether as a result, or partly a result, of the weather or not, I had a stroke on July 8th. Its immediate occasion was of the kind which is supposed to bring on apoplexy. I got, that is to say, into a towering rage.

The previous day, Alison had been round to the Social Security offices and got me a form N 127 A, on which I could apply not to pay national insurance from the previous April, that is to say from the beginning of the financial year in which I was to attain the age of sixty-five. On Thursday morning, I filled this form in.

The whole system of the Welfare State is a gigantic swindle, which benefits nobody but strikers, the workshy, petty crooks and the large number of clerks which it employs, but, as I have now drawn an old-age pension for three years, I was wrong, that Thursday morning, in concluding, from the form and the literature with it, that I was to be deprived of old-age pension till I was seventy, because I was theoretically self-employed. I made no money, but I was compelled to pay for self-employment stamps, since I had no other status. Even if, in the end, I were to draw an old-age pension for a year or two, it was in fact the case that I could never recover what I had already paid into National Insurance over the past thirty years. I raged loudly.

My sister took the form in and did her shopping. When she came home, I said I felt wobbly. However, I ate my sandwiches and went upstairs for my usual afternoon rest. I slept a bit. In the course of the evening, my right eyelid and the right-hand corner of my mouth drooped. Two brief diary entries I tried to make were illegible. My speech was blurred. According to Alison, I was very pale, and there was a cold sweat on my forehead. A pain crept down my left arm, such as I believed to be characteristic of *angina pectoris*. My sense of balance was disturbed. When I went to bed, I had the greatest difficulty in getting out of my trousers and into my pyjamas. It was as though I were drunk.

I fancied I must have had a slight stroke. In the morning, my sister went round the corner into Alexandra Road, and by ten o'clock Dr Roper was here. He also concluded that I had had a stroke. He prescribed Valium and said that he would look in again on Monday.

I tried the Valium once, found it made me sleepy and stopped it. I could not read. My attention to things around me wandered. On the other hand, I could not sleep at night, so that it would have been sensible, had I thought of it, to take Valium as sleeping-pills. I cannot now recall whether, when Dr Roper called again on the 12th, I told him that I had stopped taking Valium or not. What he must have noticed himself was that my speech remained blurred.

I cannot remember whether, that Monday morning, Dr Roper performed any tests which showed a marked incapacity in my right hand, but I could hardly use a pen at all (the diary shows this). I could not swat flies, which were plentiful at the time. I cut myself shaving. I could hardly type.

48

Later in the week, I nevertheless walked with Alison as far as the Lord Sidmouth, a small public house one approaches by way of the beach on the far side of the castle almost as far as the lifeboat and returns from past the naval hospital. It had always been a pleasure to walk out with Alison, who, within a few days of her seventy-first birthday, was a sufficiently good-looking woman for me never to mind when she was taken, as she often was, for my wife, having no marked family likeness with me.

That Friday, without her encouraging presence, I performed what I preened myself on supposing an almost impossible feat for a man who little more than a week before had had a stroke. I set up the compost bin in a new position I had prepared for it on a patch of soil against a northward-facing wall, the six-foot street wall topped with broken glass, beyond the concrete path which leads past the two sheds to the garden gate, by the quince tree, which was clearly to bear fruit that year. It had not borne fruit last year.

On Saturday, having come down to their holiday home, my daughter, my son-in-law and their three children were to be here to lunch. I set up a bonfire in the incinerator and, when he arrived, allowed Donald, my grandson, then aged eight and a half, a keen pyromaniac, to start it.

The wind was in the south-west, and, as the fire got going, the smoke blew on to the washing next door. Angus, who was in the kitchen at the time, pouring out tonic waters (I do not think he and Erica Jo had yet entirely given up strong drink), fell about laughing as he saw three of our neighbours tumble out of their house and with frantic haste gather the washing in.

And that reminds me that I ought to switch the refrigerator on if I am to enjoy a gin-and-tonic in less than three hours, which is not long enough for tonic waters to get really cold. As to my coat and so on, it would be sensible to get them out of here. My coat had better go into the cloakroom, which is where it normally lives. My walking-stick can also go in there, and so can the plastic bag. The vacuum flask is no doubt already sufficiently drained. I will take the desk diaries for the two last years (the one again bright red, the other dark blue) into the crime room, leaving the current one open where it was on the imitation Jacobean refectory table beside my typewriter in the back room, then nip through there if, through the bow window, I see Julia at the wrought-iron gate or suddenly hear a key in the front-door lock.

But who knows? Julia's sense of smell may be so acute that she can detect the recent presence of a clean person in a room, even though he doesn't smoke, which I desperately want to do. Perhaps I should also take the previous diary into the crime room now and sit on the narrow divan bed gaping at the row of *Notable British Trials* volumes, their French equivalents, the Sacco & Vanzetti books and the rest. If I shut that door, which also is a sliding door, she would detect me only if I sneezed or had a coughing fit or started wheezing. I might even smoke in there, though I must not displace an ashtray, except perhaps the one out of the cloakroom.

HERE, IN THE back room, I feel half-way between safety and danger from an intrusion by Julia Colvin. I have an inner glass door of the conservatory and the sliding door to the crime room ready open. I could not see a form at the wrought-iron gate, but I should be able to hear a key in the lock. I can smoke, so long as I blow the smoke into the conservatory and do not leave matches, cigarette butts or ash in any of the ashtrays in this room.

I sit in the chair in which, I suppose, I have spent most of my life these past three years. It is not so easy or so low as the big chair in the front room, and it has an extended wooden arm on which, if I wanted to, I could write a little, carefully. I have done a great deal of smoking in this room. The walls and ceiling, the blue and white, flowered damask or brocade of the curtains, even the glass of the pictures, are

50

stained with nicotine. The ceiling above my head, where I sit with my back to the conservatory windows, is quite brown. To a non-smoker, the room probably always smells faintly of stale tobacco.

On the stripped pine mantelpiece of the absurd, but quite decorative, unusable fireplace to my left, the nearest visible object in the room is a lamp of bedside type, whose shade also is nicely stained. As near, but visible only if I turn my head, is one of no fewer than seven framed Toulouse-Lautrec reproductions on the walls, two on this near wall, one on the wall straight in front of me, above the closed and bolted hatchway (normally useless, since we never eat in here, but I do occasionally open it to enable my sister to pass drinks through, when it is sometimes a pleasure, depending on what my mood is and how fond I am of her at the moment, to see her framed in the kitchen, working at her preparations for dinner), and four on the right-hand wall, which is further away, these four evenly spaced, with two blue-shaded wall lamps and a mysterious electrical fitting (I have never understood its purpose) between them.

There are two other pictures in the room, one (quite a big one, a *gouache*, centred above the mantelpiece) of three distorted women's heads by a Glasgow Sunday painter called Taylor Elder and one (not so big, but bigger than the Toulouse-Lautrec reproductions, in blue crayon, on the wall straight in front of me), of a comical bull by an Italian sculptor, whose signature, if it is there, must be under the mount. The picture I regularly point out to visitors is the Toulouse-Lautrec over the hatchway, where it belongs by reason of the fact that it is the only one of these seven reproductions to be a horizontal composition.

It represents a white-coated barman with two top-hatted customers and advertises *The Chap Book*, whatever that may have been. The barman looks French. We always hear of the cocktail shaker as an American invention of the 1920s. Yet here is a barman using one in the Paris of the

1890s. The two customers look English. M. Granville, of the Lords art gallery, once informed me that the model for the peculiarly John Bull figure on the right had been the Baron de Rothschild's coachman.

Against the right-hand wall stands a small oak bookcase, made by me, in which are standard British (not only English, for it also contains a volume of early Scottish and two volumes of medieval Welsh-language) poets and dictionaries, including a Welsh dictionary, as well as Goethe's *Faust* in the original and Dante's *Divina Commedia* in both English and Italian. From where I sit, I can see the right-hand edge of the books with which the front wall of the front room is entirely lined. Also in this room are the twenty-four volumes of the fourteenth edition of the *Encyclopaedia Britannica*, in a bookcase of their own, against the wall straight in front of me, on which stands the transistor radio.

In the middle of the room is the imitation Jacobean refectory table. On this stand, as well as my typewriter and the current desk diary, left open (for Julia Colvin would never look at it, and, anyway, it contains nothing which I would not wish her to see), six boxes of typing paper, bond and bank in three sizes, quarto, foolscap and A4. These and the sight of my typewriter tempt me to sit at the table and start typing.

Except this past week and for a week in June, I have tried or intended to type something every morning, often in the evening too, during these three years. With the exception of one short story and two or three book reviews, nothing that I typed in that time has been worth publishing or has been published. Yet I used to be prolific and much published.

To type now would be foolish, because the sound of my typing would very likely stop me hearing a key in the lock or the opening and shutting of the wrought-iron gate which preceded it. What should I type? The account, perhaps, of a modest or at any rate moderate-sized seaside town's annual regatta. For I see that my diary for our first full year here has approached that point in the town's history and that I took a certain interest in it, having just missed it the year before.

To pick up all that might have made my account amusing, I should have needed to attend, if not all, yet most of the week's, indeed eight days', events, but I was not quite up to that, after my stroke. I do not even know what happened on opening day, Saturday, July 17th. On Sunday night, I suffered from agitated insomnia. On the 19th, Dr Roper called again, accompanied by a new and temporary member of the consortium, who, upon hearing Dr Roper prescribe Mogadon for my sleeplessness, called him into whispered consultation, as a result of which something else was prescribed. This turned out to be a kind of capsule, tiresomely mounted on cardboard and called Welldorm. I tried one of these capsules and decided next morning that I would return to Mogadon, of which I still had a few left from the previous year. They are pleasant to the taste and can be sucked, as well as broken in half. But the outside temperature dropped that day, and I needed no more sleeping pills.

There was a little rain in the afternoon and then a lot in the early evening. The sound of rain beating on the conservatory roof was delightful. One listened to it and watched it pouring down outside in a kind of ecstasy.

What regatta events may have taken place the previous day, I again do not know. There were no outdoor events that Tuesday, but only a jazz session at the Quarterdeck, so nothing was rained off.

Next day was fine. Once more, I do not know what regatta events may have taken place that day, but in the evening Alison and I walked along to the Lord Sidmouth again.

The great day was Thursday. In the afternoon, in Alexandra Park, there was a grand display, with the band of the 2nd battalion of the Queen's Regiment, the "Eagles"

53

parachute display team, the Royal Green Jackets free fall parachute display team and the band and display team of the Southern Youth Highlanders.

To this I did not go. I was more or less compelled to witness the carnival procession in the evening. I do not know what the attendance had been at any of the earlier events. It was enormous for the procession.

This set off at seven o'clock from the extreme north end of the town. At least an hour before that, a constant stream of people had started coming up Clarendon Road. The procession made its main stop just past the castle at our crossroads, as if to impede the traffic as much as it could. That is to say, the float bearing the carnival queen and her princess stopped there, and there was a long speech over loudspeakers.

I went out briefly to stand with the crowd at the corner. Turning, I saw the Porringers and Faggs, as I then supposed them all to be, grouped evenly in their first-floor windows, very conspicuous because there was nobody at the windows for some way to their right or left. They would have made an interesting photograph.

The carnival queen's float had been preceded by a police car, the fire brigade and a regimental junior band. I had missed all but the sound of them and missed a large proportion of what followed, but I do remember that after our own regatta queen came those of the French and Dutch towns with which this one is "twinned". Followed fancy-dress parades for children in various age groups, girl pipers and majorettes, a band of sea scouts and much else, including the carnival queens of other towns along this coast or inland. Some of this we were able to watch on tiptoe at our bathroom window and a window on the landing outside, but I did not find it possible to stand craning there long.

The various bands had been carefully spaced, so that the sound of one had almost died away before the next was heard approaching. As it happened, an excellent performance of Haydn's *Creation* was in progress on Radio 3 at the time and blended here beautifully with the scene of popular rejoicing outside. Hawkers did a great trade in balloons and squeakers.

From beginning to end, including the stop, the procession took fifty minutes to pass the end of Clarendon Road. It would then pass along the rest of Jubilee Road and High Street and somewhere to the south turn left and left again along Queen's Parade to return to the castle, a total distance of a mile and a half. By the time the comic and historical floats, those put out to advertise various shops in the town and the equestrian class (I tried to see that, but saw nothing and concluded that equestrians in the neighbourhood had boycotted the carnival procession) had gone by, one heard the junior regimental band approaching along the sea front and up Castle Road.

The dispersal took a long time. We heard our air-force cadets drumming their way along Hassell Lane to the drill hall, and then the raging traffic started up again.

Most of the town's twenty thousand inhabitants would be involved, as parents, other relations or friends, with somebody taking part in the procession, while summer visitors and foreign students took an interest. As Alison said, a lot of work must go into organising a procession like that.

Next day, she and I went to Erica Jo's house inland for lunch. We were brought back by Angus, with Donald and the younger girl, a tot of four. At a little before five o'clock, we joined the great many people who had assembled on the sea front, towards the pier, which itself was crowded. Promptly at five o'clock, there was a sudden roar to landward, and nine aeroplanes, painted red and trailing red smoke, appeared in arrow formation and, flying out to sea, almost at once climbed high, losing their smoke. At a great height, they turned over and descended, trailing blue smoke. They changed formation, and two of them flew out of sight to north and south, but were presently to be seen

55

returning just over people's heads on what seemed a collision course, miraculously avoided. These were the celebrated Red Arrows, an RAF acrobatic team. They went on repeating the same manoeuvres with great precision for twenty minutes and then withdrew as suddenly as they had appeared. It had been exciting. It left one stimulated.

To the north of the castle, there is first a field, which is used for fêtes and which was once a paddock for the horses of those stationed at the castle, then a small road, with only two houses in it on the far side, then a few grand houses, the indoors swimming-bath and the headquarters of the yacht club, a small road with no houses in it, but only the public conveniences and one side of the swimming-bath, then a children's paddling-pool and a large green which extends to the lifeboat house. This green also is sometimes used for fêtes, bigger ones. That week, it had been a fairground. Luckily, as the wind had not been in the north, we had not been troubled by the fairground music, which nowadays consists of pop records enormously amplified, instead of that formerly produced by steam organs, evocative if not beautiful.

On Saturday morning, my sister and I walked along the promenade to the lifeboat, which normally stands not in the lifeboat house but on the high shingle in front of it, across the promenade, from where it can be the more readily launched. We had always missed seeing the lifeboat launched and were there to see it launched that midday as part of a display of Safety at Sea & Air Sea Rescue, a concluding item in the regatta. A good many other people had had the same idea.

It was hot (the drought had clearly returned), and we had to wait an hour. The actual launching was preceded by a parachute flare and a far greater number of maroons than are ever fired (there are only two) when a real rescue is afoot. The launching was over in a matter of seconds. Alison and I turned southwest and walked across the silent and largely deserted fairground to the Lord Sidmouth,

56

which comes near the beginning of a long row of sea-front shops, which have highly desirable flats over them.

Five helicopters flew overhead in formation, emitting trails of green and yellow smoke. There was a curious boat out at sea, with an ornamental square sail billowing. It might have been intended for Cleopatra's barge or the bucentaur in Venice. I believe that boats like that are now quite common, but I had never seen one and found the image haunting.

This had been, as it happened, the town's 150th annual regatta, and we artlessly supposed that it must have represented a special effort. The next year's regatta would be advertised as for the royal jubilee, but in the two succeeding years, for which no special occasion had been discovered, we were to find that the annual regatta would go on much as before, with unimportant and diminishingly interesting differences. Proclaiming occasions was simply an attempt to boost local effort, which does not seem to need boosting.

At the Sidmouth, Madge, the landlady, who runs the pub with almost no help and of whom we are fond, told us that after the carnival procession on Thursday beer had been poured over the carnival queen and that there had been a shindy and seven arrests at a public house next door to the Pavilion, where there had been a queen's grand carnival dance.

There is no shortage of local louts, who are somehow more depressing than London louts. You feel that there may be that in London life which causes louthood, whereas the louts in places like this are merely imitating those of London.

That afternoon, from my bedroom window, I observed that Mrs Fagg, next door, pegging out clothes, was pregnant. That Saturday and Sunday were good days for butterflies, doubtless because of the buddleia blooming in the garden. Sunday was the 25th of July, anniversary of the date on which our furniture had been moved in here.

Tuesday was that of the date in which we had first slept in the house. It was also my sixty-fifth birthday.

I should have liked to spend the greater part of Monday at my typewriter, reviewing our first year here. I could not yet type well enough. I managed a letter that day.

THE SCHOOL HOLIDAYS had begun. They had begun on the day of the carnival procession. The streets were full of local schoolchildren, who latterly might be of any age up to sixteen (as a result of legislation introduced surprisingly under a Conservative government by the admirable Mrs Thatcher, who had also been made responsible for the idiocy of decimal coinage, talked of as though shillings and pence affected international trade, which is conducted only in pounds). There had been local schoolchildren on holiday the previous summer, but I had no doubt thought of them as a part of the influx of summer visitors, which all seaside towns dread. There were also some of these, but most of them were spare-time fishermen, wearing quaint costumes with brightly coloured woollen caps, who congregated on the pier or in boats and on the shingle and were easily avoided.

Letters in the local paper blamed the foreign students, taking holiday courses at schools in the neighbourhood, for the habit working-class children had formed of riding their bicycles on the pavement. There were two boys and two girls who regularly did this on the far pavement of Clarendon Road, and I used to dread my sister being run into by them on her return from her shopping, when she had to cross the road, which had its own dangers. She never has been and has always negotiated the crossing with great care. I had first met children riding bicycles on pavements in a Buckinghamshire village, which had no foreign students, four years before, and I imagine that the habit has now become universal throughout the country. Very few foreign students can have brought their bicycles abroad with them and seemed in general pleasant.

58

Mrs James had three foreign students at her guest-house, a very nice French girl and two German boys, aged fifteen and twelve, the sons of important men in their own country. They, she complained to Alison, upset everybody in the house, were rude to her and ate like pigs.

On the 1st of August, a Sunday, there were dragonflies in the garden. On the 2nd, there appeared a plague of ladybirds, the second that year. On the 4th, two friends from Paris appeared and took us out to lunch at the Metropole, where the dining-room wonderfully overlooked the sea and where the food was better than I had found it at the Portsmouth Arms, a hotel just to the south of the pier, where my fellow writer used now and then to dine me and where, I must admit, we always had good wine.

On Friday, August 6th, the younger sister who then lived with Dr Millard took upwards of a hundred aspirin tablets and died, leaving a note to say: "Look after Wally." She had been the tall, thin woman, who walked so very upright with her stick because she suffered from a chronic form of Menière's disease and was afraid of falling suddenly.

Wally was presumably the long-haired tabby cat which was often in our garden, scratching up the soil and depositing small turds, and which I had sometimes thought I might beat to death with a spade if I ever caught it when I had a spade in my hand. I now saw that I must let him live, out of respect to Kathleen Millard's memory.

Also in the local paper at that time were letters about the fouling of pavements by dogs, presumably foreign dogs. Only once had a dog been in our garden, when the back gate was open for the dustmen, but they had, indeed, defecated on the pavement outside the house. To have their dogs defecate on pavements, at night, presumably satisfies some obscure impulse in their owners, for it is difficult to see what other purpose they served in towns. Guide dogs for the blind, a favourite local charity, are clearly an exception, though the number of guide dogs exhibited at the annual fête in the castle paddock greatly exceeds the number of blind persons to be seen requiring those feats of obedience in the town. Dogs are theoretically useful also as a protection for old ladies living alone, but in practice such old ladies never have them, old-age pensioners being generally unable to afford the foodstuffs which go in at one end to produce the mess at the other. There are five million licensed dogs in this country, producing goodness knows how many annual tons of stuff worse than useless as manure, since they are flesh-eaters and their excreta caustic, like those of cats. The number of cats, sent out at night over neighbours' walls, is unregistered.

5: Police

THE CHILDREN NEXT door all had bicycles, on which, I am bound to say, I never saw them riding on pavements. After many trials up and down the garden path, even Jeremy was able to give up the tricycle and take to the small bicycle which had no doubt formerly been his sister's. Then, on occasion, all three might go out together. If they did, they were soon back. When Mrs Fagg was not around to insist on them taking Jeremy, the two girls were inclined to go off without him, while the Whistler had been known to go off on her own.

We had concluded, not with perfect certainty, that her name was Angela. Alison said that she had a beautiful complexion, but her eyes were narrow. This I established one morning when she was skipping (not an accomplishment she often practised) outside our kitchen window. I shut the window rather noisily, and she glanced over her shoulder.

It is extraordinary to what extent one may know people's faces only in profile over a garden wall (for instance) and how different their full faces may be. This was so much so in the case of Denise that, when I first saw her face-to-face a year or so later, I was not to recognise her. As I had seen her in the next-door garden or in Hassell Lane, she was simply a well-grown pre-adolescent with legs a bit too long, neck too short, unexceptional girlish features, head a bit flat but with hair sensibly cut in a short style, fair rather than otherwise. The Whistler's hair was a little darker, Jeremy's a little fairer.

Though his expression was generally sour and despite the sallow complexion which often made him look less sparklingly clean than the rest of the family, one occasionally saw that in profile Porringer had an amusing little, tip-tilted nose. Mrs Porringer had rather a pinched face, though with sweet expressions. She was probably the nicest of the family. Her hair was tinted fair, cut in a short style and discreetly waved. I should have thought her older, but I noticed from my bedroom window, when she was pegging out clothes, that her arms were smooth.

She and her daughter both had calfless legs, as though neither had ever done any walking, though Mrs Fagg's ankles were slender and Mrs Porringer's were not. Mrs Fagg was the only member of the family who smiled, though I did not find her smile particularly attractive. When she smiled, she chattered, as indeed she did when she was not smiling. Her hair also was cut in a short style, discreetly waved and tinted darker than her mother's. At one period, when she had let it revert to its natural state, one was to see that it was dark and thoroughly grey.

A great deal of money was clearly spent at the hairdresser's in that family. It is only recently that I have come to the conclusion that even Fagg's fair, wavy hair is the result of treatment. For a short while, it looked darker, less wavy and less freshly washed than usual.

Apart from the calflessness of her legs, which is less conspicuous when those legs are fully exposed, as they frequently were this summer, Mrs Fagg's figure is good. Her face is jowly, her nose broad.

In the summer of 1976, when her figure was not at its best, I have it noted that, as early as the 29th of July, the clothes line was full of nappies, no doubt once Jeremy's. I should not have judged it yet time to get them out and wash them. However, there could no longer be any doubt that a new little Fagg was on its way.

Fagg's complexion was almost as fresh as the Whistler's. His features in profile were regular, and his head was not badly shaped, though perhaps a bit low of brow. Facially, in profile, he was the best-looking of the family, though it was a pretty rather than a handsome face, and I cannot imagine that he was attractive to women (he was certainly not attractive to my sister), partly, of course, because of his short, stocky build, but also because his expression, when relaxed, was rather stupid and because his expressions were often not relaxed. He walked about either looking harassed or with a ferocious scowl. The odd thing is that these expressions had not lined his face.

We had begun to doubt whether the Whistler really could be his sister, whether the sister had not been a young woman who stayed in the house for a few days in early June. There was no family resemblance between the Whistler and him, and he must be at least fifteen years older than her. She might be a sister or half-sister of the two younger children. What they called her might not be "Auntie" but "Angie". From their attitude to him and his to them, we had formed the impression that he was not the father of Denise and Jeremy, that it was a second marriage. They did not call him Dad, as they called Porringer Grandad. He paid very little attention to them, except to shout at them when their behaviour annoyed him, as it not infrequently did.

Denise, too, not infrequently bullied Jeremy and occasionally struck him so as to make him cry. He was, indeed, clearly a sister-eclipsed boy, as well he might be with two big girls about and a mother from whom he took all his instructions. He was not, I fancied, allowed to go out alone. At any rate, he was often left in the garden by himself. He then played in an extraordinarily foolish way, digging a little hole with a stick or arranging stones and bits of wood into what to him was no doubt a pattern, but, when any adult was in the garden, talking ceaselessly in a shrill, unintelligible whine. He would do this even when the adult was Fagg, who did not answer. If it was Porringer, he would address him as Grandad at the beginning of every sentence (and it was the only word I would hear). Quite often, he talked to himself. Once in a while, he climbed a short way up the apple tree and would peer at me between the branches. His eyes were narrowly set.

It seems likely that none of the children were allowed on the pier or the beach, the adult Porringers taking not the least interest in the sea they had come to live beside. They were inland-orientated. If they went out, it was by car. There was never a bathing-costume among the washing on the line. Buckets and spades one might not expect where the beach was all banked shingle, but there could have been some items of fishing-tackle or floating toys here and there on the grass, where there were only bicycles and a tricycle and a pair of stilts and two balls which were not played with since so many had gone unreturned, in addition to odd pieces of wood and a greenhouse in sections and Porringer's watering-cans, bowls and buckets, a cistern and a hut, pieces of piping and sheets of corrugated iron.

We have never discovered the Christian names of Mr or Mrs Porringer or Mrs Fagg. This is natural enough, since the only one ever to sing out names has been Mrs Fagg, who would not sing out her parents' or her own.

ON THE MORNING of August 12th, the locum from round the corner called unexpectedly and said that I should have a chest X-ray at the local hospital. This annoyed me. I did not like him and hoped that his temporary position with the consortium would be short-lived. I doubted very much whether chest X-rays were usual five weeks after a stroke.

My mouth still drooped at the right-hand corner, but my speech was not bad except when I was tired or when I talked for too long. I was still a bit inclined to cut myself, shaving. I could sometimes swat flies. I made fewer mistakes at the typewriter, but my handwriting had not much improved.

I still make a lot of mistakes when I type. I correct them

with the small, chalk-covered leaves called Tipp-Ex, but the under-copies of my typescripts are a mess. My handwriting has never quite returned to normal.

The 12th, Thursday, began with a mist, but by midday the temperature was back in the eighties. Our neighbours laboured on, though in just what they were doing I had somewhat lost interest. What I did notice was that Porringer had stripped to the waist and that his skinny torso, pretty hairless elsewhere, bore repulsive tufts of grey hair on the shoulders. Fagg was more modest, at first wearing a shirt. When he got down to a singlet, one saw how fat he was around the shoulders and upper arms.

In the late afternoon on Friday, Mrs James's two German students, sitting in her garden, had pop on a radio or record-player blaring at full volume through open doors in the conservatory. Unwisely, in view of my recent stroke, I went out through the back gate and blew my top at them over the guest-house wall. This stopped the awful din for the moment, but it started again the following morning. Luckily, that day, we were going to Erica Jo's for lunch, Angus and his family being in the neighbourhood again.

In the course of the morning, Fagg loaded up his car with great care, taking a long time over it. Eventually, he departed with his wife and the three children, rather a tight squeeze. They were much waved off by the Porringers.

When we had come back from Erica Jo's, the pop nuisance started again. The same tune (if pop may be said to have tunes) on what must therefore be a record player. The same again on Sunday morning.

Alison went round to see Mrs James, who is rather deaf but not as deaf as all that. She was in great distress over the two German students. She had put them in the conservatory because they upset everyone else in the house. They would be leaving on Wednesday, but she went and took the plug off the record player meanwhile.

We had thought (and hoped) the Faggs and Angela were setting off for Malta or the Costa Brava. But their holiday lasted only a day and a half. They were all back again that evening, and the children were at their noisiest next day.

Porringer was making something. It involved a lot of hammering, but also skilled carpentry or rather, I suppose, joinery. He worked partly on the trampled soil of the garden and partly on the raised concrete below my bedroom window. What he was making turned out to be a large, horizontal window. Towards the end of August, he began knocking out bricks to this side of their old kitchen window, which was small. So that was where his new window would be going. The effect should be rather handsome. The hammering took place in the early afternoon.

At the same time, a gang of men moved in and began to knock down the Hassell Lane wall and the old shed in the doctors' back garden, next to the Porringers'. They were followed by a bulldozer, which uprooted trees, removed a lot of soil and roughly distributed bricks and rubble. These having been more carefully placed by hand, much of the soil was put back and covered with smoking tarred chips. A roller rolled these, and what had been an overgrown garden was then an asphalted car park for doctors and their ancillaries, patients still parking on the weedy gravel at the front of the house, on Jubilee Road.

The uprooting of trees and the pulling down of the shed (itself hideous) had done unwelcome things to the view from the back of our house and the garden. Henceforward, we had an unimpeded view of the building on stilts which jutted out from the nearer Social Security house and a less impeded view of the drill hall at that corner, as well as of people and working-class houses across the road.

The bulldozer or a truck had demolished part of Dr Millard's wall. This, however, was presently put to rights in leisurely fashion by a bricklayer and his mate.

My X-ray showed nothing. Porringer's hand was in a bandage, but he finished his window. At last, the school holidays were over, and at a little after twenty past eight on the morning of Wednesday, September 8th, he drove off with the Whistler, while at about twenty to nine Mrs Porringer and her pregnant daughter set out on foot with the two younger children. For three days, I should be able to enjoy my little sleep in the afternoon.

THAT THE FAGGS and Porringers had had to come and live so close to us was a misfortune we had not deserved. For nine months, we had lived with the back or, more properly, that side of our premises silent. We had had every reason to expect that the house next door would be bought by a quiet couple like the Mrs Windmill and her late husband (my sister knew Mrs Windmill) who had lived there until a matter of months before our arrival. Now we were sandwiched, in a narrow converted coach house, between Clarendon Road and seven active people, with another on the way.

I tried to think that there was nothing hostile about them, that they were merely absurd and that, of course, there were too many of them. It might be that they simply lacked imagination, not that they had coldly determined that they would go their own way and that nobody could object to whatever they did (the fact that there were so many of them would, certainly, make it possible for them to ignore the rest of the world). They might settle down. It might be that one day Porringer and I would exchange a few amicable words over the garden wall or that Alison and one of the women would meet in a shop and that thereafter we should be on such terms that some consideration for us would seem normal to them.

(The fact of the matter has been that, in three years, neither my sister nor myself has ever so much as exchanged glances with either of the two women. As to the few words exchanged by Porringer and me over the garden wall, they were not to be amicable.)

The Wednesday on which the schools opened in September 1976 was blissfully quiet during the daytime. I collected the seeds of mignonette, alyssum, tobacco plants, rocket, sweet peas and everlasting flowers, the dill and borage and pinks being already in pill bottles. After tea, I began to sort my seeds. Porringer started hammering with the short-handled sledge-hammer he had used for the bricks at the side of his admirable kitchen window.

This time, he was knocking down the parapet at the side of the two steps up from the garden path to the raised concrete in front of the porch. (The bit of wall supporting this parapet remains just so much jagged brick to this day.) There were concrete blocks lying about in the garden. A rectangle here had previously been concreted by Fagg, who that week had been driving off again at a quarter to six in the morning and reappearing in the afternoon. Sunset that week was not until half-past six (as it is this week), and by lighting-up time Porringer had mixed cement and got some of his blocks into place, one or two of them needing to be cut with hammer and cold chisel.

He continued on Thursday and Friday evenings, and I concluded that the structure was to be a coal bunker, though two concrete blocks projected inward from its small aperture. I should have supposed that even Porringer could see that these would prevent a shovel getting to most of the coal. (It *is* a coal bunker, and they do. A result of their discovery of this fact was to be that, late one night, shortly after the bunker had first been filled with free coal, Fagg would have to knock out two blocks from the ends of the structure, so that they could be pulled out and shovels thrust in at three points.)

There was some rain that weekend, though not so much as on Monday, when it went on hard until ten o'clock in the evening. It had not prevented Angus Black from bringing us not only a great bag of mainly cooking apples, but two dustbinfuls of rather stony soil from their garden, on what I feared might be their last visit before Christmas. I riddled the soil and spread it in various places where the soil level was below that of the concrete parapets.

Wasps were attacking the grapes on our one vine. Between showers, I picked the grapes. Alison started juicing them with a simple press she used mainly for oranges. The Gayelord Hauser juice extractor was no good for soft fruit. Ours was anyway in use for Angus's apples, with which at the weekend my sister was to start making apple jelly.

The children next door were fairly quiet that weekend for the second time, but they made up for it on Tuesday evening. They had two friends with them, and they ran up and down the garden path and along Hassell Lane, shrieking. The noise was such that it penetrated Mrs James's deafness, so that she appeared at one of her bedroom windows, bawling at them to be quiet. Mrs James has a loud voice.

Having helped his father-in-law concrete the massive lid of his crazy coal bunker, what Fagg did next was sink a piece of iron piping in a mass of concrete in the garden. This was to be the base for a whirligig clothes drier, to be used in addition to the clothes line, indeed lines, for there was an arrangement whereby washing could be hung on white, movable lines over the raised concrete.

The whirligig was very clearly visible from our kitchen window, as it need not have been. It was also inconvenient for Mrs Fagg and Mrs Porringer, who had to step out on to the grass and soil in order to peg clothes on it, so that they did not use it much. For the past two years, the iron piping has served no other purpose than, in the depth of winter, to support a tray on which crusts of bread and other food refuse could be placed for the birds.

WE HAVE A quince tree. It stands on a patch of soil near the sheds and leans over the six-foot wall into Clarendon Road. Until it was discarded, the compost bin stood by it. I cannot see it from the downstairs back room. I could see it from the conservatory if I cared to place myself so clearly in Mrs James's line of vision from her bedroom window, which she is quite likely to be flinging open at ten o'clock in the morning, having tidied and washed up after her breakfasts. I could see it even better from the westward-facing window of Alison's bedroom.

Without seeing it for the moment, I know that it is bearing more fruit this year than it bore any of the four previous autumns. The year of our arrival and two years ago, there was no fruit. Last year, there were a few quinces. Three years ago, there were a hundred and fifteen. All but two or three of them grew on the street side, which is the sunny side. Many were split, no doubt because of the drought or suns excessively hot, but this did not make them useless.

The quinces had not long been turned yellow. It was on the morning of September 24th when a woman came to the door and said that she saw we had a quince tree and did we mean to use the quinces, because some people didn't, but just let them drop? She was small, well-dressed, well-spoken. We had in fact been discussing whether to make jam or jelly and had rather decided on jam, because that amount of fruit would make more jam. I told our caller that we did mean to use the quinces.

When she had gone, I got the stepladder out, took it into Hassell Lane and then into Clarendon Road by way of the back gate and picked five quinces. They did not come away easily, and most of the others were very high. As my balance was even then a bit shaky, I thought I had better wait until Alison was back to stand beside the stepladder and perhaps hold a leg or my trousers, before I reached up from the top step.

The following morning, a man came about quinces, an educated or at least well-spoken type in holiday casuals, broadly and vertically striped, like warm, dark pyjamas. Had it been any day but Saturday, I should have supposed him a belated summer visitor, but even middle-class residents might not be at work that day. Not until he'd gone did I perceive the significance of him wondering whether he could buy *some* of our quinces and of him saying, when I had told him, very nicely, that he couldn't, "Oh, you want them all?" He would imagine, of course, that what he could see, hanging over the roadway, were only a fraction of what there were on the garden side, where in fact there were none, the tree there being exposed to the north. What he could see from the road were all our quinces.

I did not pick any quinces that day. In the evening, my sister went with Mrs Nicholson to a music society party. Mrs Nicholson had left Ethel Fleming and gone back to her own house in the residential suburb along the coast. Ethel was somehow managing, having kind neighbours at her new block of flats.

On Monday, with my sister standing beside the stepladder and holding on to my trousers, I picked fifty quinces, but then did not feel that I could reach any more. It was on Wednesday afternoon when David Beckford rang wanting to tell Alison something.

In the course of their conversation, Alison mentioned that we had been gathering quinces and had found some too high to get at. David thereupon said that he had tall clippers, which he would bring round at once.

This he did. Standing on the pavement of Clarendon Road, he thrust the tall clippers up among the branches of the quince tree and worked the simple mechanism which causes the clippers to clip. He had no success. I fetched the stepladder. David is a bulky man. He also has quite a bad polio limp. But he got up the stepladder, and, with a resolution, even a recklessness, which I had been quite unable to command, he got all the quinces down, handing most of them to Alison (I held the steps), but some falling on to the pavement or into the roadway, some even rolling across the road. There were about sixty, many of them badly split, one or two quite rotten.

Next morning, the 30th, a Thursday, I started pruning the tree, with the idea that next time it bore fruit these

71

should grow lower. This, I fancy, is why it was to bear no fruit the following year and very little the year after. I cut off quite a lot of wood and dragged it round to the concrete directly in front of the conservatory, cut it into short lengths with the sécateurs or the pruning saw and brought my incinerator out. I placed a firelighter over the centre hole in the bottom, tipped in a wastepaper-basketful of paper, cigarette packets and matchboxes and packed in all the green branches I could. After lunch, I started a bonfire.

At about the same time, Fagg, who had been at home all week, doubtless while his wife was having a baby, started hanging a sheet out on the clothes line. The worst of the blend of smoke and steam having spent itself, partly but by no means wholly in the direction of the washing, the incinerator settled down to emitting only a little smoke of a faint blue. I went in and left it.

There came a ring at the door. It was Fagg, with shirt sleeves rolled up over his chubby but certainly powerful arms. He wondered, not with any marked impoliteness, if I could arrange to have my bonfires a bit later in the day, because the smoke blew over on to his washing.

I could hardly be said to have bonfires in the plural at that time. The last had been two and a half months before and had been the only once since our neighbours arrived. Except by pouring buckets of water down the funnel of the incinerator, I could not, had I been so inclined, have stopped that bonfire, which would presently burn itself out. There was just as likely to be washing out next door later in the day. Quite often, it was left out all night.

Fagg and I had never spoken to each other before. After four months in the next house, his first words to me were a complaint. With much more to complain about, I would never have complained before I had become acquainted with him.

I told Fagg that, as a matter of fact, we were a little tired of the washing next door, particularly of the strings of knickers and underpants that were so often stretched across our kitchen window. He said that clothes had to be hung somewhere. I suggested that, if they could not be hung elsewhere, the best thing might be to send them to a laundry. He said that some people preferred to do their washing at home, I that I clearly understood that this was the case with the two women next door, who were washing maniacs.

I am never at my sweetest in the early afternoon, when I feel that I should be resting upstairs. Warming to my subject, I further informed the young man that we found him and his family filthy neighbours. It was not, I said, only the washing. By knocking down the end wall, he had exposed us to the incursion of cats. There was also the constant hammering at other times, the bawling kids and the fact that the garden next door looked like a builder's yard.

He said that it would not be like that when the garage was built, but that they had a lot to do. He said a great deal more, but from this point his discourse became increasingly uneducated and incoherent. After listening to it for a while, bored with its lack of meaning, I told Fagg, thinking that it was the kind of expression he, with his working-class culture, would understand, to piss off. This, muttering something which I was unable to catch, he did, carefully shutting our wrought-iron gate behind him.

I ought not, said Alison, to have used that expression. I agreed. It was unfortunate, but I had been provoked. I fell a prey to gloomy thoughts.

Improbable as it may seem, it cannot have been more than a matter of minutes later when the doorbell rang again. It was a policeman, rather young and personable, thin, dark, immaculate, quiet-mannered. He enquired whether I had a bonfire and also whether I had been having words with Mr Edward Fagg (so that really was his name). I said yes on both counts and invited the policeman in. He took his cap off, but would not sit down.

The course of that conversation I cannot quite so clearly

73

recapture. I never could. I did not understand it. I was not, for a start, told what it was that Fagg had complained of, the bonfire or insulting behaviour.

If I had been taxed with the particular expression I had used, I should, I thought, deny using it. I would never use such an expression, I should say. I had told him to *push* off. He, not knowing that middle-class expression, had substituted one with which he was familiar. But I was not taxed with that or with anything else. After assuring us that his sole concern was with neighbourly relations, the young policeman went on about bonfires.

The bye-laws about these, he admitted, were far from clear, but went outside with me to see what the physical situation was, said that the use of an incinerator made no difference and suggested that bonfires should not be lighted before sunset. He said that I might care to consult my solicitor, though what I was to consult him about was not clear. If Fagg wished to make a complaint (had he not made one), he would need to go to the environmental desk at the area office. The policeman did not think he would go there.

Thereafter, the conversation became more general, if that were possible. The policeman told us about the trouble his own wife had with a neighbour who lit bonfires every day when she hung out her washing. This seemed improbable, though it was the time of year for bonfires. In any case, if the policeman could not stop that man having daily bonfires, there did not seem to be much he could do about my first for two and a half months.

"We live very quietly here," said Alison.

"They're just a mob next door," said I. Fagg was mad, I further suggested, because the smoke had come just as *he* had pegged out a sheet. Jokes were made , about what I can't remember.

"Well, I'm very pleased to have met you," said the policeman, put on his cap and went.

Somehow into all this entered (had perhaps already

entered into my conversation with Fagg) the existence of a three-and-a-half-days-old baby, presumably next door. My sister thought that Mrs Fagg had had her baby at home and that it was she who had sent her husband round to complain. It was also presumably she who had made him ring up the police when he told her how I had greeted his complaint. I thought that he had behaved as he had because it was his first child and he felt that the world should make a fuss of him.

I was a bit fussed. Although he had left us with the utmost amiability, the policeman would have to write a report on the incident when he got back to the station, and I should be on record as a person who caused or at least gave rise to trouble.

ONE OF MRS Nicholson's two sons was a farm manager in the township where Erica Jo has a house. His wife came at that time at least once a week to this town and joined Mrs Nicholson and the others for coffee at the Parlour. That Saturday, Alison asked if anyone knew whether there was a time of day at which bonfires could legally be lit. Mrs Nicholson's daughter-in-law, an attractive young woman called Janet, said, yes, six o'clock in the evening. On Tuesday, Alison took a pot of quince jam to David Beckford's office. David was not there, but his assistant confirmed that the time for lighting bonfires was six o'clock.

On Thursday, with more quince and some lilac, which had also grown up to an inconvenient height (and was also not to bloom the following year), I therefore started a bonfire just as six struck from the cupola of the naval hospital. It was the best bonfire I had had to date, with flames leaping upward from the funnel of the incinerator.

I had another bonfire on the stroke of six the following day. It was a swirling wind that evening, though predominantly south-west. The green wood first produced great clouds of steam, and these, rushing up between the north wall of our house and the garden wall, collected in the Porringers' garden. Through our kitchen window, I saw Porringer on the grass, as though he meant to rescue a few socks and other small things which had been left on the whirligig. When the clouds of steam had changed to a steady emission of blue smoke, they were still there, so that I suppose he was driven back.

The next evening was still. The smoke rose straight up and cannot have bothered anybody.

That was a Saturday, of course. On the following Monday, October 11th, Alison brought in thrillers from the public library. While I was looking through them and while she was washing clothes at the kitchen sink, there was a crash. It was not in the kitchen. We looked here. We looked there. Then my sister saw that it was the tall mirror, with gilded stucco frame, hung above the low half-landing near the foot of the stairs in such a position that people could see themselves full length from the little hallway, a successful placing, I felt. A bent nail had kept it in place for over a year, but the mirror, having been down for cleaning, had thereafter held for no more than two days.

The glass itself was broken into two large pieces, with various splinters in between. The stucco was only badly chipped at a point half-way up one side.

This episode delayed lunch for quite a while. Apart from gathering up the bits and apart from superstition (seven years' bad luck, of which we have had almost three), we both felt upset and did not quite know what was best to be done, looking-glass then already being presumably expensive to replace.

As a matter of fact, nothing decisive has ever yet been done about that mirror. An oval one, in an inlaid mahogany frame, has been in its place for the past three years, I believe on the same bent nail, though I dare not look, in case the oval mirror crashes, too.

6: A Glimpse of the Pier

I CANNOT NOW think how I collected all the material I burned. No doubt there were annuals I had pulled up, big ones such as tobacco plants and borage, as well as clippings and sawings off of trees and trimmings of bushes and climbers. At any rate, according to my diary for that year, I had no fewer than seven bonfires in the second half of October and at the beginning of November. During that period, the funnel of my incinerator came off, and the centre hole at the bottom became so enlarged that there was danger of the firelighter falling through. I clearly needed a new incinerator.

Despite the bonfires I fitted in, autumn so far had been extremely wet, as though it were trying to compensate for the droughty summer. The 5th of November turned fine, however. That afternoon, my sister and I went to a chrysanthemum show at the Pavilion, and then walked on the pier. Some of the chrysanthemums were very fine, though Alison's chief interest was in the pots of preserves also exhibited. She had wished particularly to buy blackberry jelly, of which I am fond. Unlike the previous year's, all the preserves were to be auctioned at eight o'clock the next evening, when we did not propose to go back. There was, in any case, no blackberry jelly on show. There was morello cherry jam, which I should have liked to try.

My reason for wanting to walk along the pier was to see the town from the end of it and to make a few mental notes of what I could distinguish. This was connected with a notion I had for a novel, which was to begin with a man walking in the morning from the end of the pier towards the town and to conclude with him in the evening returning to the end of the pier, with what intention I had not yet decided, might indeed never decide or at least never state. It might be suicide.

There were quite a lot of men (one woman) fishing on both sides of the pier along its whole length. Their costumes varied, but generally included brightly coloured woollen caps. One bunch of louts had a transistor discoursing the awful monotony of pop music, but it is something that there was only one and that it was on a bit of seat near the shore. The greatest concentration of fishermen was on a lower level of the pier, at the end.

From this point, at one time, a passenger ship called the *Lord of the Isles* had sailed twice a week for Calais in the summer. The only time I had been along the pier before was to see this ship sail, intending later to take a trip on it, but Blod, my wife, had then fallen ill. That was eleven years ago, when we were staying here in a rented cottage. I had not then taken much interest in the view inland from the end of the pier.

Being now both senior citizens, we had been allowed on the pier for 3 pence each, a fraction of the normal charge (the tickets said CHILD AND O.A.P.). A boat whose petrol winch had been hauling it up the shingle as we passed on our way to the chrysanthemum show had set up a little stall and was selling herrings at 8 pence each. We bought four.

Alison marinaded them for dinner, and a very nice change they made. It was Guy Fawkes night, and we saw that the Porringers had a bonfire. We went upstairs and watched from the north window of Alison's bedroom. The children were sitting in a row on the coal bunker. Their mother and Fagg were not present. By way of fireworks, there was only one small packet of sparklers, of which Mrs Porringer lit two.

From our point of view, it was a satisfactory bonfire. It was at the far side of Porringer's garden, and, as there was no wind, the smoke went straight up. It was not a big bonfire, and, in the morning, we saw that Porringer had not burnt the more solid pieces of old wood that had been lying about.

I WAS NOT altogether well. I had a touch of urethritis or cystitis, and hanging over me all this while was the threat of at least a cystoscopy, cheerily uttered by Dr Roper. I had had a cystoscopy before, about twenty years earlier. I remembered it as the most unpleasant experience of my life. On arrival home, I had been flooding my trousers with blood, and for a week afterwards I had pissed fishhooks. Roper assured me, however, that nowadays they no longer used steel cystoscopes and that I should have a general anaesthetic.

If I had been willing to go to a hospital further inland, I could have had my cystoscopy earlier, but I had elected to go to the one in the nearby town, where Alison would be able to visit me easily, and an appointment there would take longer. In the meantime, one night a little more than half-way through November, I had to get up in the small hours, as I did often enough, and, going into the bathroom, found my sense of balance curiously adrift. All morning, I swayed when I walked and had to put my feet down carefully. After lunch, with no more than the usual amount of alcohol in me, I was stumbling. It was the same after I had lain on my bed and slept briefly.

Alison went to see Stella, chief receptionist to the doctors round the corner. Dr Roper came at a quarter past four. He got me to walk and turn. He also got me touching his finger and my nose with alternate hands, at first with my eyes open and then with them shut. His diagnosis was that my arteries were furred up. He prescribed some pills, which he said would probably do no good. The cause of my furred-up arteries was heavy smoking.

I had myself thought that what I had had was perhaps a very slight further stroke, with no symptoms apart from the disturbance of my balance. It could, said Roper, be that the furring up of my arteries had been responsible for my stroke in the first place. I found, the following morning, that I was again making far more mistakes on the typewriter than I had been lately, and, when I had to sign a cheque for my sister, my signature was again very shaky.

Alison has good teeth. There was, nevertheless, a small cavity between the two front top ones, and one of these was chipped. At the beginning of December, she therefore went to the dentist called Porteous, at the near end of Castle Road. She found him satisfactory (gentle, she said, but firm).

I had four teeth, all in my bottom jaw, one to the left, three to the right, two of these adjacent. Until two years before, I had had another one adjacent to the tooth on the left. This had suddenly become troublesomely loose, so that I had had it removed, by a young man called Mercy, more painfully than any previous tooth, at a consortium of dentists in London. Otherwise, I had managed with four or five bottom teeth, for the best part of twenty years.

I had had false teeth before that, while I was still in my forties. I had had more than one set. I had always found that I could not keep the top lot in without gagging. My top lip being a bit long and my bottom lip short, I had sometimes worn the bottom teeth alone, partly at least for cosmetic effect. Then the bottom lot had broken while I was eating a sausage in a public house, and, as I fumbled with a handkerchief, I had decided to do without false teeth, as I did for almost twenty years more. I could not manage hazel and brazil nuts, unless grated, or pickled onions. I could not eat very tough meat. I had the crusts cut off my sandwiches, occasionally nevertheless eating pieces of French bread. On the whole, I managed very well.

Latterly, however, I had been having a bit of toothache, and the backmost tooth on the right was somewhat undermined by a cavity, while the two adjacent teeth were loosening slightly. I therefore had my sister make an appointment with Porteous for me. This would not have been until February, but Alison said that my teeth ached and that there might be one or more to come out, so an appointment was made for the following Monday.

I was the first patient in. Porteous had a look with his little mirror at my four teeth and asked me which of them I wanted out. I told him how long I had managed as I was and that I was hoping he would fix up those four teeth to last. I had, I said, tried false teeth and found that I could not wear them. When I put the top ones in, I had gone on gagging until I took them out.

Porteous was a Scot, with a broad, pale face and a voice of quite astonishing monotony. He said that he would pull out any teeth I wanted pulling out, but that otherwise he could do nothing. It was no use saying that I could not wear dentures, since almost everyone else did. Perhaps I would like to think about it. I would do that, I said, and extricated myself from the dental chair. Two girls in the surgery gave me sympathetic smiles, and one of them said that there would be nothing to pay.

I thought that I would try another dentist. I did not. I was to do nothing about the matter for another year and a half. For a year, the bit of toothache would subside and the two adjacent teeth not become noticeably looser. For the moment, I had medical concerns other than those affecting dentistry.

Two days later, in the afternoon, Alison went with me by taxi to the local hospital to see Mr Satterthwaite, consultant surgeon. I was again first to be called. The nurse in attendance took me to a cubicle and asked me what my trouble was. I said it was waterworks. She told me to take the bottom half of my clothes off.

I did just that, removing my trousers and underpants, putting my shoes back on and sitting down to wait. When the nurse (a married woman, neither very pretty nor quite

81

plain, thin rather than otherwise) returned, she told me I should also have taken my jacket off and put on a kind of bathing-wrap that was hanging on a hook in the cubicle. These things I did and was then taken in to Mr Satterthwaite. I was shown to a chair facing him across a table.

"Mr Atha is rather deaf," said the nurse.

"Oh, not really," said I.

My exchanges with Mr Satterthwaite proceeded in normal voices. Towards the end of our interview, I had to take the bathing-wrap off and lie on my left side on a bed, bottom towards its edge, and hoist up my knees to, the nurse said, my chin. I could not quite get my knees up to my chin, but she said this did not matter. Then Mr Satterthwaite dipped his fingers into a kind of green Vaseline, shoved them up my arse and felt around. He washed his hands while I put the bathing-wrap on again and sat where I had sat before.

A form had to be filled in, and the nurse had not got it. Getting it took her quite a while.

Thinking that such things might be relevant to my case, I told Mr Satterthwaite that I was impotent but not incontinent. He told me that my impotence would be due to the condition of my arteries, which Dr Roper blamed on my heavy smoking. Mr Satterthwaite was a small man, not at all distinguished in appearance, in late middle age, very nice, a Yorkshireman, though without north-country accent. From near Sowerby Bridge, he said, which was quite near my own home town.

The nurse came. The form was filled in, and I was got out of that room and into the cubicle. There, the nurse began speaking to me as though I were very deaf indeed, telling me what I next had to do, which was to reappear at the hospital between nine and ten o'clock in the morning one day soon, as it might be tomorrow, in order to have blood and urine specimens taken. These would be sent to the seaport hospital. An X-ray would then be arranged there, and an ambulance would fetch me. I must have looked as though I were not taking this in, for presently the young woman left me in the cubicle and went to sit beside my sister, to whom she repeated everything, leaving with Alison the two forms which had to be handed in when blood and urine specimens were taken.

A letter came from the bigger hospital on the 14th of December. Attached to it was a little package containing four laxative tablets, of which I was to take two the following evening and two the evening after. The X-ray was to take place in the afternoon of the day after that, on Friday. I was to have nothing to eat or drink after 8.00 a.m. on Friday, and the total amount of fluid taken during the twenty-four hours prior to the examination must be restricted to one pint. Transport had been arranged.

I took the first two laxative tablets on Wednesday evening. Their effect began at three in the morning and went on long after breakfast, producing a very great deal of internal pain and outward soreness. Even at the risk of being insufficiently scoured and feeling, even so, extremely brave, I took only one of the remaining two tablets that evening. Its effect was only tolerably painful.

On Friday afternoon, parched and I hoped sufficiently purged, I lay for an hour on a table bed beneath a massive and rather beautiful X-ray apparatus, while a tall, stony-faced girl with a lot of blue on her eyelids told me to breathe in, breathe out, hold my breath and breathe away and left me at intervals, while at one point a wild-eyed Indian doctor very slowly injected what I am sure he said were fifty cubic centilitres of dye into a vein in my right arm, this being known (I was later to learn, and it had to be injected slowly, or it made you sick) as an IVP or intravenous pylogram. I was then strapped up with an affair into which air was pumped, with the intention that two inflated pads should block the ducts from my kidneys to my bladder, a further series of pictures then being made.

Eventually, I was released, shown to a lavatory in which I

83

was instructed to empty my bladder (always supposing that I could) and brought back to have one final photograph taken (which would, as it happened, show that I had in fact emptied my bladder). I dressed and returned to the room in which Alison was waiting. A cheerful ambulance driver drove us back here.

As I well knew, what had impended was a prostate operation, and these sometimes go hideously wrong. That there was some obstruction, but that it was benign and that he would not, in any case, operate because of the stroke I had had had been decided by Mr Satterthwaite when I first saw him and communicated by him that same day in a letter to Dr Roper. This wretch had therefore known Mr Satterthwaite's main findings, or could have known them if he had read the letter, since December 9th, eight days before the business with the X-rays, but had not communicated them to me or told me that the business with the X-rays was instead of a cystocopy, though I had somewhat guessed that it was.

I heard them on December 23rd, but this was only because, by mistake, Stella had sent up my notes instead of my sister's when Alison went to see Roper. I was not to see him myself until after Christmas. As to the fact of my blood and urine being normal, I was not to hear that until after I had next seen Mr Satterthwaite in February, having forgotten to ask him when I saw him. I never did hear why I continued to feel a stinging sensation when I made water.

However, my worst anxiety was over by Christmas, and I was able to enjoy the presence in the neighbourhood of my Black grandchildren. My anxiety had been and was still enough to keep me from paying too much attention to the nuisance of the children next door, at half-term and weekends and during the Christmas school holidays, in any case diminished by bad weather and long nights. I did notice that no start had been made on the garage and that no attempt had been made to get rid of the rubbish in the garden.

84

THE SECOND HALF of January was mild and damp, and I took an interest in things out of doors. The first of these was the compost bin. This consisted of eighteen narrow panels of a hard plastic substance which slid into one another to form a cylinder, assembled over a trench across which a metal grille had been laid. An inflatable top was then placed over the whole structure and pegged into place with plastic studs. These might be removed and the inflated top raised, so that kitchen waste, leaves and so on might be put in. When the top was raised, it was also possible to lift one or more panels and dig stuff out at the bottom.

"Drop garden waste in," said the advertisement. "Shovel rich compost out." And it showed an attractive young woman doing just that, half-kneeling gracefully, two of the panels somehow caught up so that she had both hands free, one wielding a small shovel, the other holding a bowl into which she put the crumbly compost.

That compost took longer to produce than the booklet said I had already established the previous spring, when I first dismantled the bin and moved it to what I thought a better position. The second time round, I had chopped my orange peels smaller, shredded leaves from their centre veins and stopped putting in the emptyings of a vacuum cleaner and a carpet-sweeper which the booklet had encouraged me also to use. For nine or ten months, there had been going in day by day, mainly put there by my sister, the outer leaves of cabbages, cauliflowers and lettuces, apple and potato peelings, coffee grounds, tea-leaves, the tobacco picked from each day's sixty or so cigarette ends and, of course, decayed flowers, the vegetation of herbaceous plants and trimmed autumn leaves. There had also gone in a dustbinful of dry grass cuttings from Erica Jo's and hundreds of small yellow apples from what we were cautiously treating as a purely ornamental crab-apple tree. Many of these I had stalked and bashed with a spade, but not, I must admit, all, hoping in due course they would rot. During the summer months, when Alison went to put her carefully chopped kitchen waste in, she had been much bothered with a cloud of small flies, which we thought would help decomposition, if not internal combustion. I had not, I may say, omitted occasional sprinklings of the "accelerator" called Garotta.

I had meant to empty or partly empty my compost bin in late February, manuring my roses before I pruned them and forking compost into the soil before the spring sowing of my numerous seeds. A week before the middle of January, however, I noted that rain had collected on the inflatable top and that in fact it was somewhat deflated. It had to be removed. I took this to be a cue for dismantling the bin six weeks earlier than I had intended.

I had got too large a bin, and it was only half-full. When the tastefully sage-green panels were removed, what had been there retained its cylindrical shape, though a few recent orange peels fell off, and numerous little apples tumbled out. The grass cuttings were clearly distinguishable as such and remained dry. If there was any rich, crumbly compost, I could not see it. The material at the bottom of the heap was perhaps a little more decayed than it had been last year. When I had pulled away the less decayed stuff from the top, there was some smoke to betoken combustion, but if anything less than last year, and the rain soon quelled this.

It was in intermittent rain that I broke up the coagulated mess and, a bucket at a time, distributed it to some extent among my roses, but predominantly over a part of the main bed where no bulbs were already coming up and where, indeed, nothing was visibly growing at the moment. I came indoors to rest for a while. When I turned and next looked out through the conservatory windows, the places where I had scattered compost were alive with female blackbirds, who were tugging the compost about, much of it over the low parapet on to the concrete.

When I went to the conservatory doors, they flew away.

As soon as I came back indoors, they were back again, with a sentry posted. Heaven knows what they found so appetising about the compost, but they dragged it about over the paths and the parapet and littered the concrete with it.

A male blackbird is attractive in its jet-black spring plumage, with bright yellow beak, and will sing splendidly of an evening from some high point, presumably asserting its territorial right, not to attract the dingy females, who are so much more numerous, the most numerous, I had recently read in some newspaper, of all birds, outnumbering sparrows and starlings. I hated this blackish vermin plodding around my compost, as it did for days, and littering the concrete with lumps of various sizes

The immediate upshot of all this was that I decided not to reassemble my compost bin, not even to try to find and mend the puncture. I tied the whole lot up, panels, grille, inflatable top, studs in a little bag, and put them into a shed. If anybody wanted it, I would give it to him. If not, I would try to get the dustmen to take it one Wednesday morning.

I should, if anything, buy peat and use chemical manures. The kitchen waste and leaves would have to go in the dustbin, but otherwise our lives would be simplified and cleaner.

The fact was that I had somewhat lost interest in my garden. Because of the Porringers mainly, but also because of the opening up of the doctors' back garden, this was no longer the *hortus conclusus* I had thought it. I could no longer attempt to make a real garden of it. I would simply concern myself with growing bits of this and that here and there. Although I would have preferred the doctors as next-door neighbours, I should not have cared for a car-park coming right up to our garden wall, even if it had been a car-park purely in the daytime. As to the Porringers, little nuisance as they were being at the moment, it was enough that one could see them and that they could see into our garden.

In early February, two days after the day on which I last saw Mr Satterthwaite, there was evidence of what could have been a juvenile declaration of war from next door. On the concrete path which runs up the north side of the house, outside the kitchen window, I saw something odd and found a partly eaten apple on our side of the garden wall. It was a sour-looking apple, and I could well imagine anyone, after a couple of bites at it, simply wanting to throw it away. I threw it back over the garden wall, farther down, towards the gate on to Hassell Lane.

At that point, I saw also bits of sweet-wrapping on our soil. These also I threw back. I hoped that the apple at least had been thrown over by Jeremy, unable to think what else to do with it. I did not think he was malicious like the girls.

I HAD, I THOUGHT, perhaps started writing a historical novel ("*an* historical whatever" literary journalists and the authors of books always wrote, goodness knew why, since they all pronounced the *h* in "history") based on the journals of Capt. John Gabriel Stedman, a Scottish adventurer of the eighteenth century, and the mulatto slave, Joanna, with whom he went through a form of marriage in Surinam and who committed suicide, like Madame Butterfly, when she discovered that he had remarried with a European woman. These journals stood on my shelves.

I was getting along quite nicely when, on March 1st, my sister went up to London for three days, staying at Erica Jo's in Hampstead. I was feeling quite cheerful, but the idea of suicide is constantly present to my mind, together with the feeling that I must be alone, preferably for a few days, when I take the fatal step. I am rarely alone. I had not been alone for more than an hour or two for a year and seven months. It would probably be a long time before Alison was again away for three days.

What I had had when I first came into this neighbourhood was upwards of thirty Soneryl tablets dissolved in vodka. On the journey down, over four years ago, about half of the clear pink liquid had seeped out through the stopper of the bottle in my pocket, leaving, however, the white precipitated crystals in the solution. These I had filtered off, crushed into a powder and put in a stamp-dealer's envelope, which I had taped to the side of the smaller bottle in which I had then put the reduced solution. I kept this bottle behind some of the larger French books on the shelves in the front room.

I had read somewhere that a sufficient dose of barbiturates will kill you in four and a half hours. You have, moreover, a second chance, if you are left alone long enough, for you may, falling into a coma, linger for some days and die of pneumonia. My dose being weak, I ought, I felt, to do a bit of lingering.

That Tuesday morning, therefore, as soon as Alison had gone off in her taxi, I took out the small bottle containing my depleted pink draught. On its buoy out at sea, the foghorn was blowing. A male blackbird sang atop a chimney across Clarendon Road. Though not strongly, the sun came out at nine o'clock.

I was still in my dressing-gown at eleven o'clock. My intention was to start drinking gin-and-tonic at noon, as usual, or a little earlier, because my stomach was then pretty empty of food and my digestion at its best, and so there was little likelihood that I should be sick. After three or four gin-and-tonics, I would tip the pink draught into my tooth glass, rinse out the bottle and put it in the rubbish bin, mix the draught with tonic water to make it palatable, take it and the powdered precipitate upstairs to the bathroom, swallow the powder and drain the draught, flush the little envelope down the lavatory and rinse out the glass (so that what I had done would not be immediately evident to my sister when she returned, thus gaining me extra time to linger) and put myself to bed. I was on my third gin-and-tonic and trembling with excess of adrenalin when I decided that I would not make the attempt just then.

I did not like the opportunism whereby the timing of so important a step should depend on the accident of my sister's absence. The moment ought to be chosen more seriously. This absence might still do. I could see how my digestion was that evening. Even tomorrow, even Thursday, might not be too late, for Alison would not be back until late afternoon. I finished my gin-and-tonic and ate the sandwiches she had left me, to the accompaniment of a half-pint can of Long Life beer.

That afternoon, I sank forty gladiolus corms in the raised centre bed between the foliage of the hyacinths, which was already up, and, before filling up the gladiolus holes, sowed thyme seed between them and the hyacinth foliage. On Wednesday morning, I sowed sorrel, summer and winter savory and lovage, on Wednesday afternoon tarragon, burnet, rue, balm and pot marjoram. I also pruned roses. On Thursday morning, I returned to my book.

Those who commit suicide must be impulsive people, even if they use sleeping-pills and not one of the more heroic methods, rope, plastic bag over the head, cut throat, cut wrists in the bath, knife to the heart, always supposing that they know exactly where the heart is and how to get to it, drowning by other means or climbing down from the end of a pier. I am not impulsive. At any rate, I was not impulsive at that time.

7: Summertime

SUNDAY, MARCH 20TH, was the first day of summer time. That day, after breakfast, the Fagg parents, drove off with the baby, Jeremy and the Whistler, leaving Denise behind.

Denise Fagg (as I supposed her to be called) had recently acquired a friend, presumably a school friend, a girl presumably older, at any rate taller, than herself, who changed her clothes less frequently than Denise, whose hair was less stylishly cut and who lived in Clarendon Road, where she can have had no play area, for she was always next door, or the two wandered about the nearby streets together. I imagine that the friend also had no bicycle, for Denise had quite stopped going out on hers.

That Sunday morning, while Alison was preparing and cooking our Sunday lunch, the two girls played noisily outside our kitchen window, wrestling, looking in the whole time, very well aware of the annoyance they were causing. This they would not have done if the Fagg parents had been at home, for at the time they and Mrs Porringer still exercised some control over the children. Mrs Porringer had even been known to motion them away from our kitchen window. My sister admitted that she had looked at the two girls with marked annoyance.

The following Saturday morning, the two were walking down Clarendon Road. Denise looked in at our bow window as she passed. Seeing Alison with her back to the window and apparently unable to see me, to one side of the room, she stopped and stood with her tongue out.

At the weekend and now on the lighter evenings, Porringer was erecting a mysterious structure along the far garden wall. To the upright posts he began to fasten a close-meshed wire netting, so that it could not be his greenhouse. This netting was very different stuff from the ordinary chicken wire with which he enclosed his carport, and hen runs did not usually have netting over the top. From Dr Millard, who had been to the area office to find out just what he had permission to build, my sister learned that it was to be an aviary. Hen runs could, of course, be said to be aviaries, and it might be that Porringer was proposing to keep bantams, which perhaps flew higher than ordinary fowls. The structure ran for a considerable distance along the doctors' wall and incorporated what we had found like something between a bathing hut and a ticket office.

The Easter schools holiday began on Friday, April 1st, a week before Good Friday. It rained very satisfactorily that day, but not on Saturday, when there was much noise of children. To escape this in the early evening, Alison and I went to the Lord Sidmouth. On Sunday, Fagg drove the children off in the morning and returned later without them, so that we hoped they might have been put to stay somewhere, but they were evidently fetched in the evening, for the young Faggs appeared again on Monday morning with Denise's friend and a child whom I imagined to be the friend's little sister. They moved off up Clarendon Road, quarrelling loudly, but were here in the afternoon, playing hopscotch and indulging in wilder frolics.

After a tea break at five o'clock, Jeremy and Denise played in the aviary while Grandad was putting finishing touches to it. They were a nuisance to him, I should have thought, but he never checked them. The Whistler seemed to have taken to going off by herself or perhaps had in fact stayed away somewhere.

On Tuesday morning, from my bedroom window, I saw

Mrs Fagg at the top of the garden, adopting a firm stance, and heard her call out angrily to Denise, who was in Hassell Lane:

"You're not going out again this holiday, Denise. That's it."

I should have thought that Denise was out at that moment. She was throwing a ball to her friend. But perhaps Mrs Fagg regarded Hassell Lane as part of her premises. For no attempt was made to bring Denise in or stop her throwing her ball for the next hour or so, with wild shrieks, or ever to stop her throwing her ball in Hassell Lane.

Shrieks from Hassell Lane used to reach me, in this back room, through the glass of the conservatory. A fair amount of traffic passed along Hassell Lane, but I suppose it can never have been going very fast, for the children always managed to step back in time.

One day, I thought, *they will have a terrible accident.*

As a matter of fact, I used to hope they would.

That was one of the few occasions on which I distinguished what Mrs Fagg's yelling had been about. Although I heard the voices of the people next door a great deal (Mrs Porringer's least), as well as the accents in which they spoke or shouted, I could rarely detect what they actually said. This I greatly regret. I have missed a lot of characteristic dialogue.

Through the glass of the conservatory was not the only route by which shrieks reached me in this room. From the patch of garden over the wall outside our kitchen window, they would reach me by way of the hatchway (a flimsy affair), even when the kitchen door was shut, for this sliding door did not fit very closely. From the raised concrete and even more from the top of the coal bunker, they reached me rather through the windows of the cloakroom and the boiler lobby, especially if the lobby door were a little ajar, and, of course, by way of the archway from the front room. It was quite impossible to shut out those high-frequency voices. Any running, jumping or bouncing of balls along the Porringers' path sounded through the wall of this room itself, which I suspected (wrongly) was of single brick. Our only refuge was in the hall or the bathroom, which had the traffic from Clarendon Road.

I nevertheless wondered sometimes whether I would not install myself in one of these two places. Before the Easter school holiday began, I had done some pages of my historical novel, but could not continue during the holidays, during which also Erica Jo and her youngest, Dolly, came down to the neighbourhood for a few days, her husband and their other two children having gone to Norway for the skiing.

David Beckford had found a customer whom he liked for Clarendon House. We borrowed the keys from him and had a look round inside. It might be our last opportunity. The last owner had left carpets and a certain amount of furniture there, including a piano in poor condition and very much out of tune. Empty for some years, the place was in a mess, but looked very promising all the same. It had a large cellar. From windows at the back, we looked on to the Porringers' raised concrete and the path which led down to their gate on Hassell Lane. There were no Porringers or whatever on it at the moment.

As the holidays went on, there was, on the whole, more hammering than shrieking from that side. Fagg was demolishing the brickwork around the kitchen door, though without for the moment also demolishing the old porch. The original kitchen door was replaced by Porringer with one somewhat broader and glazed with ribbed glass.

On the last Wednesday of the school holidays, there was heavy rain in the morning. At lunchtime, however, Alison saw a fluttering in the aviary. There were two orange-coloured birds there, like flying goldfish.

The day after, hammering started at Clarendon House.

The school holidays had ended. A day or two later, my

sister went into a pet shop in the town to buy Pepperdust, a powder supposed to keep cats away and directed against Wally. While in the shop, she asked about orange-coloured birds and was told that they would be red factors, "a new kind of canary". By that time, there were four of them. Mr and Mrs Porringer would go out together in the evening to admire them. Presently, they were joined by two more. They trilled, their breasts visibly vibrating as they did so. Fagg swapped the small, reddish car he had then for an enormous white Ford. April ended. May began.

I had my second visit from a policeman, a burly young fellow, again wanting to know if I had a bonfire. On that occasion, however, it was not in response to Fagg's or anyone else's complaint. He had simply been walking down Clarendon Road and wanted to be sure that the house was not on fire. A faintly reproving tone crept into his voice as he pointed out that the smoke was settling in Clarendon Road.

"Oh, my goodness!" I said. "So it is!"

HAMMERING CONTINUED at Clarendon House. Much of it seemed to be in the passage on the other side of the easternmost wall of our front room. I half-expected books to fall off or my bookshelves themselves to tumble and hammerheads to appear through the wall.

Those hammers being rested for the weekend, there were shrieks on Saturday, May 14th. On Sunday, the Faggs had visitors, and one of these with a camera was photographing Fagg, who was holding his baby and, so far as I could judge, smiling or meaning to smile, for the expression was in fact a dreadful grimace.

None of that family were expert smilers, though Mrs Fagg had tried hard in their early days here and had also sung, "Early one morning, just as the sun was rising," once, quite prettily, as she moved about the garden, pegging out clothes. Mrs Porringer's face was in fact almost perfectly expressionless. So was Porringer's, though he often seemed to think that it was expressing something of deep significance. Jeremy's face was expressionless. The girls' faces were sometimes animated, but rarely in the direction of smiling, at any rate not of friendly smiling. Apart from anything else, they were a depressing lot. Fagg had at least tried to smile on that one occasion, no doubt being so instructed by the camera holder or aware that persons being photographed were expected to smile.

On May 30th, the weather turned suddenly cold. Next day, the Colvins moved into Clarendon House. The day after that, Mrs Colvin, returning from shopping, made herself known to my sister, just going out. The following morning, Alison spoke to Mrs Colvin, who was in her small front garden, planting a favourite rosebush, and invited the couple in for drinks that evening.

When one knows people quite well and likes them, it is difficult to recapture the first impression one had of them. I, certainly, was very wrong about the Colvins' probable ages, especially Mrs Colvin's. I put them both in their early forties.

I never remembered the weather so cold in June. At the same time, the wind dried up and, as it were, baked the soil, just as the previous year's sun and heat had done.

That Saturday, the Blacks were here to lunch, but that same day Erica Jo and Donald went back to London and on Sunday evening sailed from Southampton to stay in Rennes with a university friend married to a Turkish professor. That evening, Angus roasted a chicken for us to eat cold next day and in the morning fetched us by car to their holiday home, where the German *au pair* girl, Angelika, was being futile but had succeeded in boiling some potatoes.

In the afternoon, with Donald's two younger sisters, Lucy and Dolly, we all drove to a spectacular Roman site in the neighbourhood. I found it very impressive. One easily imagined the sea where a river now ran. There was a high wind. According to Angelika, they did not have wind in

Germany. She was a good-looking girl, but of irritating manner, lacking naturalness.

Not much else is noted for the rest of June. On its last day, my sister took round to St Peter's a bunch of florist's cornflowers as a contribution to the festival of flowers to be opened there next day. She had thought to take some of our roses, of which I had cut a bucketful just after breakfast. She would have liked, she said, to see our roses in the church. But the well-tended church garden had bed upon bed of splendid roses.

To the festival of flowers in St Peter's we went together late on the afternoon of July 1st. There was no mass of flowers on the altar, but exhibits at various points in the church, very well arranged. The arum lilies were particularly magnificent. We were pleased to see Alison's cornflowers forming the blue in a patriotic composition.

We first went into the church, then to a wine-and-cheese do in the maritime museum, which is almost next door, and then back to the church for a brief taste of the Handelian society singing what were advertised as choral lollipops, in fact a very respectable programme of choral music. We walked back here along the sea front. It made a pleasant evening, though my left leg pained me.

There were further musical activities the next evening. A music society concert at the castle began with fanfares by four bandsmen on the ramparts and then settled down to a concert in one of the rooms, to call them that, by a male voice trio from the cathedral town, who were very good but went on too long, and what called itself a wind trio, consisting of an oboe, a flute and a spinet, an ill-balanced combination.

Afterwards, there were glasses of wine and a variety of small things to eat. We took plates of food and wine up on the ramparts, where the moon, one day past full, stood over a quiet sea, a little lacking in brilliance. The Colvins were there.

The tasteful outward decoration of Clarendon House

was visibly proceeding. We gathered that Julia and Sidney Colvin were also busily at work indoors. They would soon be far enough advanced to invite us in. We should discover that the interior decoration of the house was to be a marvel.

SOMEBODY HAD BOUGHT Jeremy a plastic football, doubtless in the belief that he and his friends (he had none) would be able to practise a boyish (if not, indeed, manly) sport (though out of season) on one of the grassy spaces in the neighbourhood, the castle paddock, the space between the paddock and the promenade, Alexandra Park, which was at the end of Clarendon Road and then up a slight rise, or the vast area across the road from the slight rise. The ball, however, was soon commandeered by Denise.

At first, she bounced it either up and down the Porringers' concrete path or against the wall of the drill hall. Then she and her friend took to bouncing it between them along Hassell Lane, to an accompaniment of shrieks. As often as not, the ball was not thrown from one girl to the other in such a way as to bounce naturally between them, but banged on the road so as to rise into the air and be caught high up. This produced a heavier thud.

The last of the doctors' and their assistants' or visitors' cars would have left their car-park at some time between six and seven o'clock. Thereafter, the sounds of the football activity would reach me not through the glass of the conservatory but through the kitchen window and the hatchway, which indeed had little doors I kept bolted, but at the bottom of these a gap exactly at ear level when I was seated. From the change of perspective, I could tell to the minute at what time the last car left the car-park. The reason for the change from Hassell Lane to the doctors' car-park would be that in the latter venue there was no need to keep an eye on the traffic which passed intermittently along the former.

Jeremy was generally allowed to stand to one side between the bouncers in a sort of ball-boy capacity. If, by chance, Denise's friend was unavailable, he might even be allowed to be the bouncer at the other end. Occasionally, the Whistler would consent to be the other end, though not for long. Denise never tired of any game on which she had once embarked.

At that time of year, the banging of the ball and the accompanying shrieks would go on in the doctors' until about ten minutes to ten in the evening, lighting up time. At the weekend, it would go on all day, Sunday as well as Saturday, for the Faggs and Porringers were not churchgoers.

The ball itself was white, with a pattern, outlined in black, representing the eighteen panels into which the outer casings of footballs had been divided when they were made of leather. There must be many footballers now who do not know what footballs used to be like. Inside the leather casings were rubber bladders which had to be blown up with a bicycle pump. When the outer casing was hard enough, the rubber nozzle had to be tied and tucked inside, the casing then being laced up with a leather thong.

Printing on the side of Denise's (formerly Jeremy's) football guaranteed it to be of full match weight and size. This may be the weight and size of the old leather footballs, nowadays achieved by the heating inside of a mould of a given quantity of a composition perhaps still known as sponge rubber. From the photographs of footballers shown in the back pages of our popular newspapers, I feel sure that today's footballs are of the same size as the old ones, but I am left in doubt as to their weight. Today's professional footballers wear lightweight boots (as well as short pants and socks), compared with those of their predecessors. These afforded no protection to their ankle bones. They also wear no shinguards or shinpads, which were quite necessary when the toes of football boots were lined with steel. This would lead one to suppose that the balls were lighter, but perhaps today's footballers have stronger toes and are more stoical about their shins and ankles.

The only contemporary football I have held in my hands was Denise's. It seemed to be of much the same weight as the old ones, and the thud it made when bounced on a hard surface was similar or even greater. Readers of or glancers at the back pages of popular newspapers will have noted, however, that footballs now are usually decorated with black hexagons (the number of which it is difficult to estimate if you have not held one in your hands), not with lines, indeed grooves, representing the sewn leather panels of the old footballs.

That Denise's ball was of match weight and size I gathered between half-past five and six o'clock on the evening of July 5th, 1977. The evening's game had not yet begun. Denise had been bouncing the ball down the concrete path to the Porringers' garden gate.

Earlier that day, Alison had been inland to my daughter's house to pick strawberries. I had just taken some to the Colvins, not daring myself to eat many, because of the pips and my diverticulosis.

There was a knock or ring at our front door. I answered the door. There stood a girl, aged about eleven, whom I did not recognise. She had red-rimmed eyes, and these were strained with defiance.

"My football has gone into your garden," said. "Can I have it back?"

"But you," said I, "aren't one of the children next door."

She said: "Yes, I am. I've been there since February."

This was all very odd. As to her being next door since February, that was only six months ago, whereas Denise (for it was she) had been living there for a year and five or six days. My not recognising her was partly due to the fact that she was wearing a frock properly pulled out over her knickers, whereas, when she was throwing or bouncing the football, I had been accustomed to see her in navy-blue knickers either pulled up over her frock or with a separate top of some kind, sometimes a bikini top stretched loosely across her flat chest.

A more important reason for the non-recognition was, however, I fancy, that I had been accustomed to see Denise in profile. I had, it was true, seen her once full face, with her tongue out, but the having her tongue out had itself distorted her face, and I had, immediately beforehand, seen her passing down the street, her face then in profile, so that I was in no doubt whose face it was with its tongue out. I was also accustomed to seeing Denise in motion, for she was a very active girl, who, whatever she was playing at, played at it hard and long, outplaying anyone else, especially the Whistler, who was a sluggish girl and soon gave up. At present, Denise's face was stationary, looked straight at me and did not have its tongue out.

Recognition slowly dawning, I said: "I'll talk to your grandfather about it."

She went away, shutting the gate behind her. (I stress this, just as I did in the case of Fagg eight months before, because we have had to train a succession of milkmen to do it and have never succeeded in catching the early-morning postman and persuading him that it was a gate which could not be merely banged behind you, but needed the catch to be lifted and dropped into place.) It was only then that I went through to the back garden, saw the football, saw that it had not damaged any plants, read the print on the side which said that it was of match weight and put it beside the dustbin, which I saw was rather full of garden rubbish.

Whether he came there and then or later, I had expected Porringer to come round to the front door, properly dressed, and that Alison would fetch me from the garden, if I were still there, to have a serious discussion with him about what nuisances could and could not be put up with from children and the specific nuisance of the football and the shrieking that went with it. I might even ask him in. Instead, he came bustling down from his back door in shirt sleeves and, while I was meditating round that side of our garden, accosted me at the one point where, in summer, with all the foliage, it was possible to talk over the wall.

That I might have a point of view on the matter he did not consider. He was impatient.

In the tones in which he might have addressed a disobedient woodwork pupil, he said: "What's this about a ball? Give it back to her."

To which the only rejoinder I could think of was a thoughtful: "No."

He then went on: "That's stealing!"

To which, again, the only thing I could think of to say was: "U-huh."

Followed a bit about the girl being only a child, to which I did manage a slightly more articulate reply, by saying: "A horrible child."

Then a further injunction to give the ball back, from me a further: "No."

From him: "Well, you're a nice chap, you are."

And he returned up the path and the two steps to his porch door. I came indoors. This simply would not do. I had been caught unawares. Given time, I should no doubt have recovered my wits, but I did not see what I could do now. I sat and brooded.

It was a good day of the week for such a happening, in that the dustmen would be here next morning. I did not, on the other hand, fancy moving rubbish from the top of the dustbin, so that I could put the ball under it in readiness for the dustmen, who might have been inclined to question the sight of a fine new football on top of a binful of rubbish. Alison thought I should let them have the ball back. If I did, she said, we should be in a strong position. If I didn't, the trouble would go on, and, for a start, we should have Fagg round. This I thought unlikely, in view of the fact that we did not think him Denise's father or that he had much control over her.

I nevertheless went and got the ball and tossed it over the

102

wall at the far end of the garden, cursing myself for my weakness, but thinking that perhaps my sister did, with feminine intuition, perceive something in the situation which escaped me. Within half an hour, Denise and her friend were banging the ball to and fro along Hassell Lane, to the accompaniment of the usual shrieks.

THE FOLLOWING MONDAY, both Alison and I went to Erica Jo's to pick strawberries. We picked more. My sister made nine pots of strawberry jam, of which four would be given to Erica Jo.

That evening, RAF cadets hung out of the upstairs windows of the drill hall and called down to Denise and the Whistler playing with the football below, the Whistler's big tits also bouncing. Mrs Fagg called the two girls in, and there was peace, broken only by the sound of drumming.

As we had stopped listening to news on the wireless, it was not until we had our *Daily Mail* next morning that we learned of the shocking mass demonstration and organised rioting there had been that day at Grunwick's in Willesden. It was not until Thursday that we discovered from our local paper that five hundred miners from the bit of a coalfield nearest to us had taken the day off to go up to London and join in the riots. These had certainly been over a dispute which did not concern them.

To most people down here, it must have been a surprise that as many as five hundred miners were employed in those two small pits, mining soft coal. (We should discover from a later issue of the same local paper that a total of three thousand were so employed.) Even with the overmanning we knew to be imposed by the National Union of Mineworkers, a hundred would have seemed the greatest number there was room for, above or below ground. They would get in each other's way. Perhaps that was the explanation of the extraordinarily small amount of coal they managed to dig. One wondered what they did down there all day.

AFTER BREAKFAST on the following Thursday morning, July 21st, I was momentarily surprised to see Porringer working in his garden and his car just over the wall. The state schools had broken up for the summer, and that would be why he and the Whistler had come home a little later than usual last evening, with a load of carefully planed timber on top of the car.

For seven weeks, gangs of working-class children would roam the streets, thieving, breaking, destroying municipal flowerbeds, mugging old ladies, and riding bicyles on pavements, for at least twelve hours every day. For seven weeks, schoolteachers would be taking either alternative jobs or protracted holidays abroad, those who were their trade union representatives afterwards meeting at Scarborough to discuss how best to make the rest of us pay them more for doing less than the small amount of work they at present did in a diminishing term-time. A few, who were good with their hands, would stay at home, improving their properties, mainly by persistent hammering. The football I had restored to them Denise and her friend would be able to bang up and down Hassell Lane all day and every day for seven weeks, except when, mercifully, it rained.

After briefly forking his garden, Porringer set to work demolishing the old porch outside his new kitchen door. This meant taking down the blue clothes line, I supposed only temporarily. The components of the old porch were added to the rubbish in the garden.

The timber brought from school had been sawn to predetermined lengths, and Porringer's new porch was not long in assuming a shape. Its front and sides were clearly to be glazed, and there could be no pulley on the garden side. The clothes line must therefore remain down. The women already had or would soon have new arrangements for drying their washing, I supposed by the use of a mechanically heated drier indoors. This would be an improvement. I only regretted that I had so recently stuck my Con-Tact higher than need be up the kitchen window.

That year, the Red Arrows opened the regatta on Friday, but their display was less exciting than it had been the year before and lasted only ten minutes, so that I wondered if there had been an accident. It was the result of low cloud, which had made some of the manoeuvres difficult, if not impossible. I had not been aware of the low cloud, though a bit of rain after lunch had put an end to the children's noise.

The day after that was hot. The day after that, Sunday, there was again rain at midday, but the children were particularly noisy in the doctors' yard in the evening. They had two footballs, for somebody had bought Jeremy another, fractionally smaller but patterned with black hexagons like those not at the moment to be seen in the back pages of popular newspapers, there being a short break in the professional football season.

The day after that, the Blacks should have been here to lunch, but had left London late, called and been detained at Angus's parents' house in the jaguar belt. Angus alone appeared in the evening with a bag of copies of *France-Soir* which had been dumped at their Hampstead house by Betty Hitachi who was staying there while engaged on genealogical research, she being the English wife of the couple from Paris who had earlier taken Alison and me out to lunch at the Metropole hotel. These ran from February till early that month, with a notable gap in April and May, when Betty had been in America with her Japanese husband, temporarily in charge of the New York or Washington office of the Japanese equivalent of *The Times*. My interest in French crime had diminished, but cutting out the criminal columns from these copies and half-copies of *France-Soir*, dating them, filing them in the crime room, glancing at other news items and photographs and finally disposing of the rest of the newspapers would occupy me in the daytime for a week or so of the period during which typing a (or an) historical novel remained impossible.

105

Thursday that week was a grey day, but kept fine for the carnival procession, embellished that year by a small detachment of Household Cavalry. Alison, Erica Jo, Lucy and Dolly stood at the corner. Angus and Donald stayed indoors, Angus with a headache, Donald averse to crowds. I went out briefly and saw the heads of the regimental junior band, the mounted forms of the cavalry and the carnival queen, who that year was tall, blonde and unlikely to have beer poured over her. I did not note whether the Faggs and Porringers were at their windows. Julia and Sidney were at theirs. I waved to them as I came in again to rejoin Angus and Donald.

Friday was cold and windy, with the wind in the north. Porringer had reached the roof of his new porch and in the afternoon was sitting on it with a transistor beside him, from which I could hear the commentary and other sounds of a cricket test match. He was almost exactly opposite my bedroom window, which I opened and addressed him.

"Porringer," I said, "turn that thing off, will you?"

"I'll turn it down," he said.

"Off," said I, "not down."

"Why should I turn it off?" he said.

"Because," said I, "it's a bloody nuisance."

That was my second and would, I hope, be my last conversation with Porringer. I had had one conversation each with Fagg and Denise and hoped never to have another, at any rate with Denise. There would clearly never be any conversation with either of the two women or with the Whistler or with Jeremy.

Porringer presently came down his ladder, bringing the transistor with him. He did not at once turn it off, but he was never to bring it out again.

It had been a mistake to say that the transistor was a bloody nuisance, not simply a nuisance, just as it had been a mistake, ten months before, to tell Fagg to piss off. Alison, to whom I repeated the conversation, thought it was better to have called the transistor a bloody nuisance than to

106

begin by telling Porringer to turn that bloody thing off.

On the first day of August, a Monday, the Faggs were out until late afternoon in their car. The Porringers went out in the evening. That was a drumming evening at the drill hall. Big ball play started.

I did not notice whether the cadets hung out of their upper windows, calling to the girls. They may even have come out and kicked one of the footballs, and it may be that the girls were not called in soon enough.

Whatever the bone of contention, towards eight o'clock there started a frightful shouting match in their kitchen between the Faggs. There were occasional sounds of one of the children, perhaps Jeremy, whimpering, and now and again one heard Mrs Fagg's voice raised, but mainly it was Fagg shouting, clearly audible to us throughout the house and in the garden, though we could not distinguish what was being said. In a raucous, working-class voice, Fagg went on yelling for half an hour with such hate-filled fury that I felt sure the row must end in physical violence and possibly murder. I hoped it would.

There was not much noise the rest of the week. In the slight drizzle after breakfast on Saturday, Fagg loaded up the car and drove it off, returning later for his family. The children seated themselves in the back of the car and waited for Mum, who presently appeared, holding the baby. They were all to remain away for eight days, of which six were blissfully quiet.

ON THE SEVENTH day of the Faggs' absence, at seven o'clock in the evening, pandemonium broke loose in the doctors' car-park. We at first assumed that it was the Fagg children celebrating their return, but, on going upstairs to look through our bedroom windows, we saw that, among the children there assembled, not one was a Fagg. There were four small boys with bicycles and a number of shrieking infantry.

Alison at first wondered if they were visitors' children,

107

but, as I pointed out, the bikes and the ganging up made this unlikely. My sister thought that she recognised, in the very fair-haired cyclist with the loudest voice, the child of an antique dealer who lived next door to a woman we knew in one of the smaller houses along Jubilee Road. The big, rather fat girl of fourteen or fifteen, among the infantry, was, she fancied, one of his sisters.

It had taken these children some time to discover the evening amenities of the doctors' car-park and the absence of the Faggs. We did not suppose that the senior Faggs or the Porringers would like the intrusion of children not theirs. We admired Porringer's new porch, now glazed and finished, its woodwork painted white.

Its roof was felted, sloped and fitted with gutters and a drainpipe. It had, I thought, one fault, in that the kitchen door opened outwards and the porch door inwards, so that the two doors met and prevented anything much being kept in the porch or even standing in it or passing through it without shutting one door before opening the other.

What I paid little attention to in the porch, until it was switched on the following evening, was a flattish light which had been fitted against the house wall inside it. This turned out to be very powerful, like floodlighting. What it floodlit was that end, the easternmost end, of our house, and it shone with excessive brightness through the windows of the boiler lobby and the cloakroom, but would turn out not to be much of a nuisance, since it was never kept on for long, doubtless because of the amount of electricity it consumed. Its purpose seemed to be to light people up the concrete path in the dark, and its first use was clearly to welcome the Faggs home, for, although I did not see them arrive, they were all there next morning, except the Whistler.

That night, I was awakened by toothache. The tooth aching was not the one which most often worried me, *viz.*, the backmost on the right, but a solitary one on the left, which seemed quite solid and had never before bothered me, though also I did not much use it, I suppose because of its solitude.

The Blacks had been away at a Suzuki music camp in Wales, but then Erica Jo came down into this neighbourhood again with her children. It was a Tuesday when she came, the 16th of August. I had toothache again that night. The following day, they were here.

I had wondered if there might be fights between the Faggs and the antique dealer's children and their friends for possession of the doctors' yard, but by Sunday, the 21st, they were shrieking merrily there together. On Tuesday and Wednesday nights, Donald stayed in the crime room, off the conservatory, with great success, though the weather was not good, and he got no fishing on the pier. This was the first time anybody had slept in our one, inadequate spare room.

On Friday, the Faggs went off again and this time were to stay away nine days.

Two more days of ball-play and shrieking, and then the seemingly interminable school holidays were mercifully over. Though not yet wearing a school uniform, Denise drove off with Porringer and the Whistler, presumably to a secondary school in the seaport. She must therefore be gone eleven.

In the yard next to the Jameses, a dog whimpered all morning. I fancied it was the Dalmatian spotted dog which belonged to the man we called the Wifebeater, because of information we had from Mrs James.

WEATHERWISE, it had been a rotten summer, not particularly wet, but almost uniformly grey and cold. September was the same.

The Wifebeater's Dalmatian went on whimpering all month, from ten o'clock in the morning until noon, sometimes in the yard and sometimes alternating between the gate to the yard and the front door of the house, which was next door to the Jameses' down Clarendon Road and had similarly provided bed and breakfast. It was a terrible nuisance in the mornings, but it was quite an interesting and, I suppose, intelligent dog. In the evening, it was often taken for walks by one or the other of two mentally retarded youths, but, when neither of these was available, it would go for a walk, or, rather, trot by itself, starting up Clarendon Road and afterwards, I suppose, crossing Jubilee Road and proceeding down Castle Road to the grass which comes before the shingle, there defecating, then returning by a quite different road, crossing Jubilee Road again and coming up Hassell Lane by way of the corner, a complicated manoeuvre for a dog on its own.

But it was inadaptable. The first day of the new school term must have been the day on which the Wifebeater's wife left him, after which the dog, shut out of the house from ten to twelve, while the Wifebeater was out, could think of nothing to do but whimper. Or it may have been the day on which the two mentally retarded youths, posted with him by the Welfare authority, were taken away because there was no longer a woman in the house.

The dog was still whimpering in the mornings when, in the last week of that month, I saw big, luxurious caravans passing down Clarendon Road in strings of two or three and then presumably driving up the slight rise into the park for the usual end-of-season fair. The wind was in the west, and from Thursday onwards we got blasts of the dreadful fairground music of today.

The garden gate next door had been removed. Fagg knocked down the pillar of jagged brick which had supported it and started hammering at the concrete path, narrowing this. Porringer then began laying bricks at that corner and in the evenings, while it was still light till almost seven o'clock, raised up what was presumably meant to be part of his garage, but for the moment merely served to support a new and narrower gate, painted white, on the outside of which was neatly and, one would have thought, professionally lettered in black:

110

REAR ENTRANCE.
69, JUBILEE ROAD.

It was to remain like that. No more garage would be built.

It was by then October. That month was to contain the choicest weather of the year, and during its course I was to make my chief gardening effort, with, as it happened, the invaluable help of two other people. I started cutting down three espaliered apple trees, to the left of the garden from here, about a yard in on the soil which sloped up to the main bed from the near side of the concrete path to the shed, the dustbin and the gate.

These three trees had grown old and were unproductive, though the middle one had done quite well during our first autumn here. The short, thick stumps, once seasoned, would be good for woodcarving. The branches would be for bonfiring, in a new incinerator I had bought.

The wire had been stretched between three lengths of iron tubing and eyelets in the street wall. It seemed to me to be best to go for the iron and, if I could, get that out before I started grubbing up the roots of the trees, which were no doubt deeply sunk. I had only a spade, a small pruning saw and my inconsiderable weight, no axe or billhook, let alone a pick. I did not know whether the iron was embedded in concrete.

After digging away a lot of soil, I got one of the hollow iron poles out. The second one, as I heaved it this way and that, snapped and pitched me against the shed with the door. The part which remained in the soil was full of water just up to the point at which it had cleanly snapped, which was at soil level. This gave me pause.

Erica Jo, Angus and their children came down at the weekend. Angus said that the water-filled pipe could not possibly have got mixed up with the plumbing, so I got it out. He got out the nearest of the tubes, poles or pipes, which was harder and might really have been embedded in concrete.

111

My method of separating the three tree trunks from their roots was by digging soil away from the roots, sawing through them and them heaving backwards and forwards at the trunks. The last of these was done by Betty Hitachi, a big, strong girl, who again had come down for the day, bringing with her bulbs and wallflower plants.

The evenings had been drawing in. They were abruptly curtailed on October 23rd, when summer time ended. Although the Fagg children's half-term week's holiday immediately followed, we hoped that henceforward the big football would stop thudding after tea. With a bit of luck, we might get rain at Christmas and the next half-term and Easter and the half-term after that. We could hardly expect it all next summer. In any case, I should like Erica Jo and her children to have good weather wherever they were, and I should like them to be down here for much of the summer.

8: Further Glimpses

WE ARE STILL in the year before last, though not for long. It was late one evening in mid-December when I had rather a bad pain across my chest. I had had several similar pains before and thought they might be due to indigestion or excessive smoking. But, that evening, the pain was worse. A cold sweat broke out on my forehead, and the pain crept down my left arm into the hand, which made me wonder if it could possibly be angina.

There was very little of the pain left in the morning, but my sister, without consulting me, went round to the doctors' and spoke to Stella, the head receptionist, who took it upon herself to say that one of the doctors would presently visit me. It would not be Dr Roper, who was away.

First came round, in fact, a thin, married, dark and fairly pretty, terribly nice and friendly soul, who, it appeared, belonged permanently to the consortium round the corner. She made me go upstairs, undress and lie on my bed. She then carried out an electro-cardiogram, which involved plastering wires to my feet and took quite a long time. Finally, Dr Henderson appeared.

He was older than Dr Roper, darker-bearded, his hair receding a little. I had never had to do with him, though I had frequently seen him drive a shabby green car into the doctors' car-park, clearly keeping shorter hours than Roper, who perhaps had more patients. Oddly, I did not remember seeing the young woman drive her little blue

113

Mini in, but she had more than once seen me at my bedroom window. Next time, she would wave.

Dr Henderson studied the tape which had titupped out of her machine, marked with zigzag penstrokes. He pointed out some of the markings to her, then turned to me and informed me that I had had a small coronary thrombosis.

He wanted me to give up smoking. He also wanted me to live on one level, not to go up and down stairs. He went downstairs to talk to my sister and write out a prescription. I put on my dressing-gown and presently followed him.

"Mr Atha!" he said, with great severity. "What did I tell you?"

I thought this rather comical, though I did not laugh or, indeed, make any reply. I was seriously considering whether I would live upstairs or downstairs and rather concluding that neither would be strictly possible. I had no table upstairs and no bed downstairs, except in the crime room, which would be very cold at that time of year and thereafter. I had not been forbidden to climb out of bed and sit in chairs or even to sit at my typewriter and type. I was sure he would not wish me to exert myself either by moving a bed or by taking an enormous table (for we only had two massive tables, on which I could have typed) upstairs.

What I thought I would do was go upstairs, very slowly, only twice a day, to rest in the afternoon and to sleep (or so I hoped) at night. We had a cloakroom downstairs, and, for bathing, shaving and so on, I would stay in bed in the morning until the water was hot or somehow combine those operations with my afternoon rest. As to smoking, I would try to cut it down a bit and not to inhale.

On departing, Dr Henderson added: "I'll be telling Dr Roper what a difficult patient he's got."

Alison went to the chemist's and got Dr Henderson's prescription, which was, of course, free, since I had become a senior citizen. Of the two kinds of pills he had

114

prescribed, I took a yellow one, called Diazpan, after lunch. I supposed it to be a sedative. By teatime, I could hardly move about. The back of my head ached, and I had indigestion.

I have a kind of cigarette case called a memo-Smoke, bought for me, I seem to remember, by the tall, dark and handsome Angus Black at a time when I was talking of giving up or cutting down smoking. Of Swiss manufacture, it had a mechanism whereby, if you set it for a particular length of time, it would not open until that time had expired. The watchmaker's part in this arrangement was admirable, in that merely setting it would wind it up just sufficiently to send it ticking back to the starting point, at which the case would open. The case itself, however, was ill-adapted to English cigarettes and held too few. I had made little use of this, but I had kept it.

The morning after Dr Henderson's visit, I had my first cup of tea, my orange juice and my breakfast in bed, a further Diazpan and half a Mogadon no doubt having helped me to sleep better, my bladder and bowels co-operating. I then washed up and down before going downstairs for my coffee. I thus saved myself one journey up and down stairs. I was tottering in the most ridiculous manner, as I continued to do all day.

However, as I waited for my coffee, I got out the memo-Smoke. I filled it as well as I could with cigarettes and quickly established that it would still work. At first, I set the time-mechanism for a quarter of an hour, but then for half an hour. From about nine o'clock that morning, I therefore smoked cigarettes only every half-hour. If I kept this up, it would cut down my smoking by half, since I was awake about sixteen hours a day. There would no serious difficulty about doing this, though I had every temptation, there being in view almost four hundred cigarettes in two packages which had contained two hundred each. The idea would then be to increase the interval first to three-quarters of an hour and then to an hour.

I kept to the rule all weekend. On Monday morning, when Dr Roper called, I explained the mechanism of the memo-Smoke to him, and he studied it with interest. The Blacks had arrived at their holiday home. My coronary thrombosis having been reported, Angus had angelically been to see me the previous evening, as he was going back to London that morning. The others, who were staying over Christmas, could be expected that day.

Next day, the state schools were on holiday. It was the 20th of December. The Wifebeater's dog was, I see, still whimpering in the morning.

When Dr Roper next called, on Thursday, he noticed that the memo-Smoke was no longer working. This was very observant of him, for the ticking sound it had made was very faint. It was not very long, in fact, before I was back to smoking sixty cigarettes a day, though I tried not to inhale much.

If one had a perverted sense of humour, one could, I suppose, be amused by the fact that, not smoking, Dr Henderson has since had a very serious coronary thrombosis. He is, I believe, still in hospital with this.

The most noticeable lingering effect of mine was that my legs had become worse. The left one, I think, but can no longer remember with certainty, kicked when I lifted my foot from the ground. It was at this time that I took to walking with a stick I already had. I walked little.

IT IS NOON. Julia is clearly not looking in this morning. The hour chimes, and, it must be a full minute later, the twelve strokes sound from the cupola over the naval hospital, albeit faintly. I must now make my first gin-and-tonic, which will be tepid.

This involves a visit to the cloakroom and then the first of at least four visits to the kitchen, during which I shall consume three gin-and-tonics, eat my sandwiches, make and drink black coffee, do a little washing and any necessary tidying up. I had better be out of this room and

116

upstairs by two o'clock, at which time Fagg will return from the first part of his day's work and after which there is further danger of Julia looking in, not that this would constitute a danger, rather a nuisance both to me and to her. Fagg, on the other hand, always looks over the garden wall, which he believes to be his, and might just spot me through the glass of the conservatory. That would not be a good thing, though what it would mean to him, either then or later, I cannot be sure.

I do these things. I collect a few crumbs, put them with two tonic water bottles into the indoor rubbish bin, rinse and dry my coffee cup and spoon, put the sugar away and am, with only moderate effort, upstairs. On the way, I put my desk diary for the year before last, covered in bright red, with those for the two previous years, covered respectively in dark blue and bright red, in their place on the ledge. I have brought last year's, covered in dark blue, with me.

I smoke freely. It will not matter if I drop ash on the silver-birch carpet, so long as I tread it in. The butts I shall throw into the lavatory in the bathroom and eventually flush them down.

Standing well back from the westward-facing window in my sister's bedroom, I see the pale blue of Fagg's present car in the carport. The white gate opens, and he comes in, looking tense as usual, and glances automatically over the garden wall. Moving over to the northward-facing window, I follow his progress up the rest of the path and the two steps to the porch door, which he opens and shuts, then opening the kitchen door and shutting that.

I sit comfortably on the beige-covered Victorian chair and consult last year's desk diary. I see that it was the 11th of January which was so windy.

The wind was in the north-west. By the later part of the evening, it had blown up to a gale, and Alison, emerging from the Portsmouth Arms at a quarter to ten, could hardly keep her feet. My sister had been attending a music society lecture on early gramophone recordings, with illustrations and refreshments, held in the Portsmouth Arms dining room. During the latter part of the proceedings, she had heard what she took to be furniture being noisily moved about overhead, and a chimney of the hotel had blown down. Luckily Alison and a friend, who was tiny and might easily have been blown away, were given a lift home by a big woman to whom they were able to cling on their way to the car.

Kept awake much of the night by strong winds, I was nevertheless astonished next morning when my daughter and two other people telephoned us from London to find out if we were all right, having heard on the wireless that this town had been devastated. So it had, but not at our end, though the castle moat was flooded.

By midnight, the tide had risen to its highest point for nineteen years, and this fact, in combination with the gale, had caused an extraordinary amount of damage. Boats had been washed across the esplanade into shop fronts, the ground floors of houses, the children's fairground outside David Beckford's and even down side streets. Shops in High Street and Jubilee Road had been flooded, and the streets themselves were covered with mud, the sea front with pebbles. Trees had been uprooted. The dining-room of the Portsmouth Arms was a ruin.

Beyond the Portsmouth Arms, to the south of it, there were no shops on the sea front, nor were there any boats moored, so that the damage in the south part of the town was less generally visible at first, but, domestically, seems to have been worse, while, at one public house at the northern end, customers had climbed up on the roof for safety. Further south still, it was feared that the fertility of agricultural land might have been destroyed by sea water. Just here, Clarendon Road was not even damp.

Alison, of course, saw signs of the devastation as soon as she went out shopping that first morning after it. I was to see nothing whatever of it for almost a fortnight, when, holding her arm and using my stick, I managed to walk along the sea front beyond the Portsmouth Arms and back, to and from a small midday party at the house of recent acquaintances.

There was still a great deal of shingle on the esplanade. There were still boats lying up against houses and shop fronts, including one of the largest and most admired boats, which had had its back broken and was a complete loss, while others were variously stove in. Many of the petrol engines by which the boats were hauled up from the sea's edge were also damaged and would be expensive and slow to replace.

IN ORDER TO BE able to spend a little more time with us than was possible on her customary day visits, Betty Hitachi, still in England, wished to stay in this town on Sunday night, March 5th. The obvious place for her to sleep was not our crime room, which was too small and at that time of the year too cold, but at Mrs James's guest-house, across Hassell Lane at the back, its upper side rooms overlooking our garden. Accordingly, on the last day of February or first of March, Alison went round to Mrs James's and booked a room for Betty.

It was Mrs James who brought up the subject of the Faggs. It appeared our intuition had been right. Fagg was a second husband and had himself been previously married. Only the baby was his child. The Whistler was Mrs Fagg's daughter, not the son-in-law's sister of whom Porringer had spoken when he first came to our front door to ask if we minded him building a garage. She was the sister of Denise and Jeremy, and perhaps all three were Lamberts. They were rude to Fagg, who, according to Mrs James, was nicer than his wife. He worked down the pit as a maintenance man, and did a little driving instruction in his spare time.

The Whistler had been at home all the previous week and was still at home. That day, both my sister and I had seen her occupied with the baby. We had assumed, the

119

previous week, that she was away from school because she was unwell. From Mrs James that afternoon, Alison gathered that she was staying away from school to look after the baby while Mrs Fagg was in hospital.

We wondered why Mrs Porringer should not look after the baby. From her size, her bust-measurement and, indeed, to some extent from her recent behaviour, we judged it likely that the Whistler was coming up to her O-levels and ought to be at school rather especially just before that early Easter. But it was clear that very little was expected of the women in that house. They never swept the path or the upper concrete. They no longer came out to peg up washing. The men did all the shopping, except that on Friday evening Mrs Porringer went out once, with Porringer lugging the trolley.

That very day, my sister and I went for a walk round the block between teatime and drinks, just as night was falling. Not long before, Fagg had swapped the big white Ford he had had all last summer for a dark-blue car of about the size of the reddish one he had had before. To the front bumper was affixed a tin L-plate, on the upper part of which was printed:

MINISTRY OF TRANSPORT
APPROVED DRIVING INSTRUCTOR

and a number with six figures, which suggested that there were several hundred thousand driving instructors in the country.

MARCH CAME IN like a lamb, and late morning on the first Friday turned out sunny. My sister came in early from her shopping and suggested that we should at once do what I had been talking of doing on the first propitious day, *viz.*, make a note-taking excursion to and along the pier (she had not asked me why I wanted to do this, but understood that it was for some literary purpose). Not expecting her back before noon, I had in fact been thinking of doing this without her.

My anxiety that the weather should be just right was due to a feeling that to walk to the pier would so tax my legs that, as soon as I was on it, I should have to sit down. I took a scribble pad and a biro. Using my stick, I walked up to the corner, crossed Jubilee Road, walked down Castle Road and, at the Metropole hotel corner, crossed Queen's Parade to the side which is simply a broad strip of concrete, on the other side of which boats are ordinarily moored, on the shingle, to their winches, though among them at the moment there was still some disorder resulting from the January gales, while some, not only of the boats but of the petrol engines, were out of place and some damaged. The concrete itself had been imperfectly cleared of shingle.

I began pacing, stopping every hundred paces, giving my stick to Alison or hanging it over my arm and writing down what boats we were by and what, if anything of note, at that point stood across the road. Alison also counted her paces, to provide a rough check.

At a hundred paces, I was by the engine for a boat called the *Maple Leaf*. At two hundred, I was just short of a bigger boat called the *Lady Haig*, which was still sticking across the concrete and had to be walked round. Three hundred brought us to the *Beau Jesse*, just short of a glass-fronted council notice board, exhibiting scanty notices of public entertainments. At four hundred paces was the winch for *Good Turn*, and we were opposite the Sun in Splendour. At five hundred was the *Four Brothers*, and across the road was the Admiral Benbow hotel. At six hundred paces, we were already on the horseshoe ramp before the pier entrance.

At the ticket office, we declared ourselves to be old-age pensioners or senior citizens and were sold the cheapest of three kinds of tickets, which were pink. On them was printed: CHILD AND O.A.P. The woman in the ticket office had rolls of tickets of two other colours, white and buff, which were for the general run of visitors of normal age and for those intending to fish, a fact proclaimed in most cases by the rods they bore.

Once on the pier, I felt no immediate need to sit down, this was no doubt due to the interest roused in me by pacing distances and taking notes. At any rate, I went straight on with the pier itself, which I made four hundred and fifty-two paces to the building at the far end which contained the ladies' and gents' conveniences, a bar and a tea-room. The surface along which we walked was of finely grained pink concrete.

It was a disappointment to find that the way down to the pentagonal lower deck at the end of the pier was closed to the public because of repair work connected with the January gale damage, no workmen, indeed, being active at the moment, but in front of the building a small, blue Japanese truck and a red van containing the machine which powered instruments used in the repair work when this was afoot. I was nevertheless able to look down over the railings to the left of the pier (as one approached its end) and count the number of steps down to the lower deck.

Then, indeed, I did sit down, in the bar, which we found open and where we drank a pair of gin-and-tonics. This, I felt, was part of my research. I needed to know what sort of a bar it was, and I could hardly look around without drinking something.

After our one drink, we set off back. On the pier, I counted shelters, lamp posts, litter bins, fishermen and their rods. I noted that several of the oddly shaped, elongated lamps which topped the lamp posts had been shattered. I noted that, towards the landward end of the pier, the railings, elsewhere red, had been painted yellow; that, whereas there was no turnstile outside the ticket office, there was one at the exit, so that, if the day's visitors were mechanically counted, it would be going off and not coming on to the pier; that on the municipal flowerbed, between the two arms of the ramp outside, some kind of double white daisies were already in bloom, while the leaves of tulips stood up from the soil, with here and there a bud; and that the concrete surface of the ramp was of a deeper pink than that of the pier itself.

At the foot of the ramp, we turned right and walked past the boats as before, but in reverse order, counting the boats or places for boats, of which I reckoned there were forty-nine, no doubt planned to be ten yards apart. I measured the length of Castle Road, making it a hundred and eighty paces. The last but three of the terrace of ten houses was the one in which Porteous, the dentist, practised. Its front room on the ground floor was his waiting-room, and through its bay window might, as always, be seen people who sat with folded arms, bravely awaiting torture.

We arrived back here, and my sister at once proceeded to cut sandwiches. I was cheered by how well I had walked and began to put my pages of scribbled notes in order, planning how to incorporate them into a narrative. I toyed with the idea of putting it into stream-of-consciousness form, as we have to say in English, though in French the use of the historic present tense is perfectly normal.

THE NEXT DAY, Saturday, Porringer was noisily removing the outer pair of two pairs of french windows which lead (up four steps) from the raised concrete to a partitioned sitting-room of which the Porringers used the back part and the Faggs the front part (they could not, therefore, when they were watching television or entertaining their few visitors, see what their children were doing in the back garden or hear them unless the sound rose above the usual number of decibels). The day after that, Betty Hitachi came down from London.

She came down with something rather larger than an overnight case, a case on wheels, from which she first extracted copies of and crime pages from *France-Soir* between November 10th of the previous year and February 23rd of the present year. Then my sister took her and what remained of her luggage down the road to Mrs James's, where it was put into a room at the front, from which she could not look down into our garden.

After spending the rest of the day with us, Betty, who had been given a key to Mrs James's house, returned to this room, where she was to spend the night without complaint. In the morning, she can barely have been in her bath when Porringer drove off with Denise, a pair of french windows tied on top of his very pale grey-green car. She came round to us with her bit of luggage at about nine o'clock, at some time during the day visited a secondhand bookseller of whom we are all fond and in the early evening took a train for London, where she was staying, as usual, with the tall, fair and beautiful Erica Jo Black, *née* Atha.

That day, Mrs Fagg must have come out of hospital, for next morning the Whistler also drove off with Porringer. That morning, Mrs James, out sweeping round her premises, and Fagg, cleaning his car, had a great get-together, Fagg showing Mrs James what I imagined were photographs and doing his imitation of a laugh. That evening, Denise was round asking for a ball which had come into our garden. Alison said that she spoke nicely, smiled and said thank you, although told that the ball could not be looked for at the moment.

It was eventually found and tossed back over the wall. Several of the white and striped crocuses at the far end of our main bed were out.

On March 10th, a Friday, while sunset was still before six o'clock, Denise went on bouncing a ball and playing some jumping game on the raised concrete until after seven, with the floodlighting on, which suggests that both the Faggs and the Porringers were out, as they rarely were at the same time.

It rained for the next three days. We had not heard the Wifebeater's Dalmatian whimpering for some time. It was

124

the following Thursday when Dr Millard informed Alison that the dog had been put down.

That Saturday, out shopping somewhat later than was her wont, my sister saw, not for the first time, all three of the next-door children, i.e., the Whistler, Denise and Jeremy, with the tall man we had first seen around when they had their bonfire and fireworks in November. The penny dropped. He was, of course, Lambert, and he had access to his children. This access he commonly enjoyed on Saturdays and took them out, and that, rather than the atheism of their grandfather and mother, was why the children almost invariably made more noise on Sundays.

British summer time began on Sunday, March 19th, so that thereafter the sun would not set until after seven o'clock. On the first of the weekday summer evenings, after screeching angrily at Jeremy on the raised concrete, Denise conducted a shouted conversation from the coal bunker with Marianne James at her bedroom window. Mrs James was out. So were the Porringers and Fagg. Mrs Fagg would be somewhere at the front of the house, putting her baby to bed.

Only late on Wednesday afternoon did we learn with certainty that the children next door were still called Lambert. I had, I suppose, imagined that, when a woman remarried, her children by an earlier marriage, if they remained with her, changed their surname, as she did hers, automatically.

My sister went across to Mrs Owen's to take a form putting her on St Peter's electorate, as the vicar had said she ought to be, although she was not a confirmed member of the Church of England. Mrs Owen is a highly agreeable woman, living some way down Clarendon Road, on the far side, who, for the past four years, has regularly brought us our parish magazine once a month. She was the wife and is now the widow of one of the churchwardens, Fred Owen, whom I was never to meet. He had gone into hospital the previous October and no doubt been discovered to be suffering from an inoperable cancer of the stomach, but had rallied and was still churchwardening.

He was at home that afternoon, doing embroidery, which was his hobby. Also there was Mrs Owen's daughter, whom Alison had not previously met. Margaret Owen taught at the nearest girls' grammar school. That, apparently, and not the secondary-modern school at which Porringer taught woodwork, was the school to which both the Whistler and Denise went.

She understood, said Miss Owen, that my sister lived next door to the Lambert sisters, who were both quite bright. Miss Owen was better acquainted with Denise Lambert, whose form mistress she perhaps was. Angela Lambert was in the third form (and therefore, presumably, despite her pectoral development, no more than thirteen or fourteen years old). Denise Lambert was a delightful child.

Alison is not given to flatly contradicting people or telling them that they are fools, but did venture to say that, as a neighbour, she found Denise Lambert rather noisy. As she said to me afterwards, drawing upon wide experience, there are perfectly frightful girls who behave well in school.

That was the last day of term. On top of Porringer's car was again a pair of french windows.

AFTER A WEEKEND of drizzle, the wind blew so strongly from the north-east during the whole of the first full week in April that Alison was unable to walk along the sea front on her way home from shopping. The north-east wind was one from which the Porringers' house sheltered us indoors and even to some extent in the garden.

The wind dropped on Sunday. It was colder on Monday. A slight drizzle starting after breakfast had turned by mid-morning to snow of a sort. From the movement of the small and impalpable flakes, it was impossible to be sure in what direction the wind lay, and from the weathervane on the cupola over the naval hospital I could not tell whether it had turned north or south, though it was clearly pointing a bit to the west. When my sister came in from her shopping, she told me, from observation of a weathervane in the town and of the movement of the waves offshore, that the wind was in the south-west.

It snowed again in the evening, more heavily, and on Tuesday morning, April 11th, the snow lay a good two inches deep, thawing rapidly in Clarendon Road and a little more slowly on the concrete parts of our garden, but not on the soil. Almost all our daffodils and other narcissi were flat, though hyacinths stuck up boldly through the snow in the middle bed, looking rather silly.

The Easter school holidays were at an end, and Porringer's car had left the garden next door by half-past eight. This was not the kind of snow the Lambert children would have delighted in throwing at each other. If I am to trust my diary, they had made only intermittent noise that holiday, while Porringer is recorded only once as hammering. This was no doubt due to the weather.

I sat again at my typewriter, hoping reasonably for peace, if not for inspiration. Through the glass of our small conservatory, I could see the snow looking solid enough on the raised flowerbed, but I could also see thawed snow dripping from the eaves and hear the occasional crash of half-thawed snow falling from the roof.

Poor Alison set off through the slush to do further shopping and no doubt to drink coffee with her friends at what they called the Parlour. Even I went round to the far shed and, pushing my spade up the concrete path, round to the two long steps outside the conservatory door and back to the shed, removed two spade's breadths of slush. That, I though, would be nice for Alison if she wanted to put anything in the dustbin.

Wednesday was still cold, but it rained intermittently, and by noon the snow was all gone from the soil. There was no further snow that week, but it remained cold. To date, according to Saturday's *Daily Mail*, it had been the coldest

127

April on record. But it was to remain an unusually cold year altogether. The veronica bush in the centre bed died. The mahonia and the fuchsias were to recover.

The following week, the children next door, at any rate the girls, were pretty noisy, but only in the evening. On Sunday, April 23rd, however, they kept me from my afternoon nap. As it happened, this was a good thing, because it was sunny, and Julia Colvin came round soon after lunch to say that she and Sidney were proposing to drive up into the orchard country of west Kent to see the cherry blossom and wondered if we would care to go with them.

The cherry blossom was not yet out, doubtless because of the cold early spring. Still, it was quite an enjoyable excursion. In the evening, the Whistler and Denise played with hula-hoops, which I thought had gone out years before, but which must have been good for the Whistler's figure and which provided plenty to shriek about, as it was to do the following evening.

On Tuesday, April 25th, I took another look at the pier. It was cold that day, too, and dull, with a strong north-east wind, but there was something unusual to be seen, and it seemed likely that, if the far end of the pier and the lower deck had not been mended, they would be temporarily cleared. At half-past four, the world's last sea-going paddle steamer, the *Waverley* of Glasgow, was due at the end of the pier.

She did not round the headland until five o'clock and was a good half-hour approaching and tying up. She rolled horribly, as she came up to the pier, and bumped heavily against the piles, some of her fine woodwork (as I was to gather from the local paper two days later) being damaged by two of these. The piles in question were, I supposed, two of the ten great baulks of wood which form what I understand to be called a falsework of timber in front of the quayside of reinforced concrete. As the ship bumped against them, these, I saw, retreated into squares cut out of

128

the concrete and then sprang forward again. I could see ironwork inside the squares, but I could only imagine how the piles were sprung or how they were fastened below the water so as to swing.

No sooner had the *Waverley* tied up than a sound like a pistol shot indicated the snapping of a long hawser from the bows to the lower deck of the pier, but this was quickly replaced. A gangway from the ship could not be placed on the pier, but one from the pier was placed aboard the ship. A town councillor wearing his chain of office then went on board and greeted the captain, a small, bearded man who had already been on the quayside, helping with ropes, so that, unlike larger contemporary enterprises, the *Waverley* must have been undermanned.

The tide was an hour off low water. When I had studied the way down to the lower deck previously, I had looked at and counted only steps to the south side, where there were sixteen. On the north side, where ropes had been neatly stretched to control passengers (and one had been raised for the councillor), I saw that there sixteen more steps descended to what at that state of the tide was sea level, the water barely washing over a concrete platform.

I had not much thought till then how my man from the sea would reach the lower deck of the pier from, presumably, a small boat in the sea, by some form of iron ladder I supposed. Far less had I thought of that platform or steps above it as the place where a real-life Jean-Paul Richard would pull his boat in and I myself step perilously off, where also I should have to rejoin him before dusk, with my sense of balance and my stick no mean feat. But much of this would clearly have to enter into the opening and closing narratives with which I had so far made little progress, still feeling, not very happily, half-committed to my historical novel.

That evening, the *Waverley* had advertised a three-and-a-half-hour trip along the coast and around notorious shoals some miles out to sea, with a bar and a disco open.

This would have been unwise in that choppy sea, in any case unpleasant for some of the three hundred passengers, who included David Beckford, and she coasted along for about half that time, then tied up again at the pier and kept the disco open for another hour. I might have gone along (not being liable to seasickness) but for the disco, an odd prospect for a vessel whose chief appeal was to nostalgia, that year very popular.

Next day, the *Waverley* had expected to make a longer voyage, but this was cancelled. It was raining. The *Waverley* sailed away.

The following Saturday must, I fancy, have been one of those on which Lambert had accesss to his children and took them out all day. It rained that evening. What noise they may have made next day I was kept from hearing by the arrival for luncheon of Angus Black, with Donald and Dolly, Erica Jo being in Norwich, where her elder daughter's music teacher was lecturing, with Lucy at the piano illustrating her teacher's lecture.

There had been rain in the morning, but it was a lovely spring afternoon. Angus, Alison and I drove to a more distant castle, which had splendid, eighteenth-century flowerbeds containing plants not, I fear, known in England in the eighteenth century. We left Dolly with Donald fishing on the pier. Surprisingly, it rained again that evening and went on all next day.

That was the day of the first Labour government's nostalgic May Day bank holidays. Most people had never heard of this holiday until they went out in the rain and found all the shops and banks and council and welfare offices shut, while the industrial proletariat, who should have been holding great rallies, must have supposed themselves on strike, as in effect they were, but on full pay and by order, not of their unions and shop stewards, but of the government.

FAGG HAS HAD his dinner and gone off in his car. I may reasonably hope never to see him again.

I leave my last year's desk diary up here in Alison's bedroom, on the Victorian chair. I walk down fourteen stairs, into the downstairs front room and, left about, into the back room, where the typewriter and all the boxes of typing-paper and the current desk diary are, on the imitation Jacobean refectory table, then by way of the nearer glass into the conservatory and the crime room. There, from the top long drawer of a small, white-painted chest of drawers, I take what were to be my last lot of *France-Soir* cuttings. In my usual chair in the back room, I study these, neatly stapled together, in the hope of discovering clues to my own past or future behaviour.

9: The Scenario

AFTER THE MAY Day bank holiday, it rained all next day as well. What happened next door thereafter falls into distinct phases.

First came the bicycles-and-tennis-rackets phase. This was conducted, in the evening and at weekend, in Hassell Lane and in the doctors' car-park. Denise Lambert and the Whistler both had tennis rackets. So had Marianne James, Denise's original friend and at least one daughter of the antique dealer who lived in Jubilee Road. They did not attempt to play anything resembling tennis, but simply knocked a ball backwards and forwards to each other, generally underhand, immediately after tea in Hassell Lane, then, when the last of the cars had gone, in the doctors' car-park. All but the Whistler were quite tireless at this idiotic play, about which they made a great deal of noise. Denise alone was constantly chewing something.

At the same time, Jeremy was out with his bicycle. He was regularly joined by the antique dealer's fair-haired boy, who was of much the same age as himself and noisier, and presently by two younger boys, who lived in Clarendon Road and whom we had frequently seen riding their bicycles up and down the pavement on the far side of Clarendon Road. These two lived off the same passage. One of them was the son of a rather nice electrician, with whom we had had something to do when we first came here.

They could not ride their bicycles freely where the girls

were knocking their tennis ball backwards and forward, and the girls, who were big enough (and Denise always ready) to use physical violence upon them, nevertheless obligingly played more in Hassell Lane, while the boys, especially at weekend, rode round and round the car-park, with occasional daring swerves out past Dr Millard's corner and into the farther part of Hassell Lane, by the drill hall.

This went on for a month or so, in cold and cloudy weather without rain, during which Fagg created a new amenity on behalf of his baby, which was in fact rather to serve his wife's convenience. The first thing I noticed was a lorry load of turf at their garden gate. If this were fully unloaded, there would certainly be enough to turf the whole of the garden area, but only a carefully calculated number of pieces of turf, a foot square or more, were deposited at the garden gate, and then the lorry drove on with turf for other customers. Fagg had already dug up, raked and weeded the half of the garden nearer the house.

He brought up his turf, carefully laid it and, with prolonged banging of his spade, bashed it into a rectangle, half the size of the Porringers' garden, omitting the coal bunker and that end of the aviary, outside our kitchen window. Next day, he sank four posts, in an evenly spaced row, into the ground immediately beyond his green rectangle. Following a number of other operations, which Fagg performed zealously and with skill over several days, there had come into existence a low fence extending across the full breadth of the turfed area and a small gate across the concrete path, which Fagg then creosoted.

The baby, whose name was as high-class as those of his half-sisters and half-brother, being Timothy, and which had by that time been toddling for almost six months, soon learned how to open the gate. An enormous stone was placed there to keep it closed, but the other children, their visiting friends and the coalheavers who delivered Fagg's supply of free coal from the pit, would omit to restore it to its place after passing through the gate, so that Timothy would be found on the soil on the other side of the fence or wandering down the concrete path into Hassell Lane.

Increasingly, therefore, Mrs Fagg turning him out on the grass, in the evening, at weekend and all through the half-term holiday, took to appointing one of her other children to look after and play with him. He was bought a variety of wheeled toys, including a large, red plastic car, which had a steering-wheel and other fittings, but whose only means of propulsion from within were, while sitting on its seat, to work one's feet along the ground. It was too heavy for Timothy. Jeremy, however, could sit in it, with his feet up, and get friends to push him round and round, to the accompaniment of shouts and laughter from him and breathless cries from them. Timothy was ignored. Indeed, he was often pushed roughly out of the way.

Denise's legs were too long to fit into the car, and so, of course, were the Whistler's. The Whistler's were also inflexible. In any case, neither of them would have found willing pushers. The Whistler was not often detailed to look after the baby, and Denise was adept at avoiding the task, sometimes by outright defiance. None of them liked looking after Timothy, far less playing with him, but doing so most frequently devolved upon Jeremy.

Once she had finished with her washing machine and got her clothes in the tumble-drier, Mrs Fagg was rarely in the kitchen or in the dining-room, except at meal times. I don't know where she was, but it must almost invariably have been somewhere at the front of the house, where she was spared the sight and sound of her children. The Faggs' bedroom was at the front of the house. So was their half of the big sitting-room.

Though less frequently than Jeremy, Denise also would have friends on what may have been thought of as the lawn (for Fagg would mow it with an electrical mower). So, indeed, would the Whistler. It was not a large piece of grass, but it was doubtless larger than the area given over to grass in any of the friends' gardens nearby, where certainly the Lamberts never played. At times, more than one lot of friends would be in the garden next door at the same time, though never for long. Sooner or later, the boys would be driven out. When she wanted to get rid of Timothy, Denise, after careful study of the kitchen window, would maltreat him until he cried and then take him indoors, where his mysterious trouble would be treated, probably by Mrs Porringer, as teething.

Angela, the Whistler, was best at games which involved sitting down. It was, nevertheless, she who produced the most remarkable noise nuisances during this period. On a fairly warm evening, she and a friend, who had presumably been invited to tea, came out and seated themselves on the coal bunker, both armed with guitars. The two instruments were more or less in tune with each other, but neither girl could play the guitar even to the extent of picking out a chord or a tune. For an hour or so, however, apparently with perfect satisfaction to themselves, they continued strumming together on the open strings.

It was also the Whistler who brought out the first transistor, other than the one Porringer had had for a test match commentary on his porch roof the year before. After tea on what had been a sunny day in early July, she came out with the transistor and a rug and settled herself against the doctors' wall, by the houseward end of the aviary, her opulent form clad in a bikini. It was not the same transistor as her grandfather had used for his cricket commentary the year before. For a while, the usual pop blared out, but it did not last very long, presumably because the temperature and the bikini did not match. The sun had already gone behind Mrs James's guest house.

Denise, meanwhile, had appeared with curled hair, so that at first I again did not recognise her, but thought that she had acquired a new friend with curly hair. I had also, from my bedroom window, seen Mrs Fagg sun-bathing in a deckchair in her undergarments, which at first seemed

135

indecent, until one thought that, after all, a clean brassière and petticoat are as decent as any other of the costumes in which sun-bathing is done by women. Porringer, all this while, had done very little hammering in the afternoon.

I HAD QUITE abandoned my historical novel. Though late spring and early summer were my best writing season, I should no doubt find it possible to write again a little when the school holidays ended in September and a little more after the end of summer time in October. It was true that towards the end of that month would occur the autumn term's week of half-term holiday, but I ought to find it possible to do a full day's writing by November, in four and a half months' time.

I did not so much care for writing things of any length in winter, when the light on my typewriter would generally be poor, even in the daytime. I wondered why the long school holidays should be in summer, when the evenings are long enough for children to shriek and old men to hammer to their hearts' content. If there had to be seven weeks of continuous holiday, surely it would be better to have them around Christmas, when the days were short, the opportunities for ball-play or hammering small and the need for outdoor exercise greater. The teachers could take their holidays nearer the equator, perhaps even in the southern hemisphere, getting to know little black boys on their home ground. Out-of-term jobs could be done just as well in winter. And this was always supposing that either teachers or their pupils required so much break from short days devoted to scholarship of various kinds.

As things were, I intended, by November at the latest, to persist with the novel which should begin with a man walking along a pier into a town in the morning and end with him, in the evening, returning along the same pier. The idea seemed to me aesthetically satisfying. Two questions arose. One concerned what he would do in the town all day, the other how he had come to be on the pier in the first place and how and to what purpose he would leave it.

A notion which recommended itself to me was that he should go home and get rid of hated neighbours and that his arrival and departure should be such as to constitute an unbreakable alibi for the inevitable murders, to which I could think of no credible alternative. In effect, the man would be myself, the neighbours Faggs, Porringers and Lamberts.

Writing a novel of which that should be the plot would not get rid of them, but it would afford me a fantasy satisfaction. It might even be that they would read it or that some literate schoolteacher would describe it to Porringer and that they should take fright and go away.

Nothing that I should say about these people would suggest that, by ordinary standards, they deserved to be murdered or to be punished in any way or would expose them to hatred, ridicule or contempt in the vast majority of eyes. All they would be accused of was making life intolerable for a writer, a person to whom continuous peace and quiet were important, of philistinism in fact. Philistinism had never been held to be a punishable offence, nor had it ever been claimed that contemplatives enjoyed special rights.

But I did not suppose that they knew I was a writer or that any of them ever read any but a school book. I did not suppose that they even knew my name or felt the slightest interest in me. They would simply be aware of my sister (whom they would imagine to be my wife) and myself as a disagreeable elderly couple who spoke with middle-class accents and lived next door at the back, always there, looking at them through windows or over a garden wall they regarded as theirs. They would feel that they had every right to persecute us, so long as they did not too obviously break the law in doing so. In law, they had a perfect right to destroy me as a writer and reduce what remained of my life to nothing.

In the novel, I need not have a sister, though a female companion of some kind would be useful to provide occasional comments. She would have to be out of the way when the murders were committed. It would be simple enough to take her to France, leave her there and I myself (the "I" or, for that matter, "He" of the novel) come over with a boatman, who would be someone like my friend Jean-Paul Richard of Wissant. This would also answer the second question, as to how my man from the sea appeared on the pier in the first place and was taken off it later, in such a way as to provide him with an alibi. They could set off one morning in the small hours on what was supposed to be a prolonged fishing expedition.

To provide the story with *péripéties*, peripeteitia or ups-and-downs, I might even allow suspicion to light briefly on a number of local people. The chief of these would be the Jameses, the Colvins, the practising doctors and Dr Millard or her sister, but might also include Mrs Owen and others, for motives which I could have the police absurdly devise.

There would also be Lambert. He might be thought to have a motive, but only for the murder of Fagg, and him I was inclined to have my narrator or hero spare, if only for Mrs James's sake. I would arrange the massacre while he was out. On his shocked return, he might be greeted by only the baby alive.

The only ones whom, in real life, I wanted to murder were Porringer and Denise, perhaps also Mrs Fagg. As I saw it, however, the "I" of the novel (if it were an "I") would need to go into their house with a revolver or automatic pistol, equipped with silencer and to shoot anyone who had seen him, except the baby, who was too young to be heard in evidence. Those who had seen him and were capable of giving evidence seemed likely to include the Whistler, young Jeremy and, alas, Mrs Porringer.

It would be on Fagg that suspicion most gravely lighted.

138

No doubt we could arrange to dispel it in the end by some display of inarticulate sincerity at his trial, but it should at first be augmented by leaving the murder weapon on the washing machine, wiped clean or handled with gloves. He could be expected to pick it up and so impose his fingerprints on it.

This could be a .22 bought at Gastinne-Renette's in Calais. It could equally be an old service revolver such as, from the career I am given in earlier novels, I might well have kept these thirty-three years and had in fact so kept, though I had never been in the habit of looking at it and should probably find, if I located and unwrapped it, that it was rusty.

I SEE FROM this red spring-binder that I had got a little further than I thought with the opening narrative of a walk home from the pier. I had got as far as going upstairs into Alison's bedroom and looking down upon a garden in which, at that time of year (I must have done it for April), were to be seen only squills, the last of the crocuses, paperwhite narcissi and one (blue) anemone. Out of sight, to the left, would have been pulmonaria, periwinkle and violets.

I am up there again now. It was the concrete path to the left with which my I or he (it was an I then) would have been most concerned. This curves down twenty paces or so to a substantial gate, normally unbolted once a week, on Wednesday mornings, for the dustmen. On the inside, it was then painted pale blue (black on the outside, as it still is). The Porringers' gate was already painted white on both sides. Their old gate had been painted black on both sides.

As there were so many of them constantly using that back gate (Porringers, Faggs and, as I now know, Lamberts), it was never bolted. Indeed, I do not believe that at that time the new gate had been fitted with a bolt (it has now, I fancy). That would make it easy for my I or he to go down to our garden gate, unbolt it, pass through, walk

139

along Hassell Lane (whatever it would be called), again for not much more than twenty paces, and pass through their gate on to the Porringers' concrete path.

I can see half the breadth of this by pressing close to Alison's northward-facing window. It must be about forty paces long, and then there are the two steps up to the concrete in front of their porch door. My protagonist would be shown walking up there, not, I thought, wearing a stocking mask, for (if she happened to come, as she may at almost any time of day, to the most prominent of her eastward-facing windows) Mrs James would think it odd and might feel driven to investigate.

(This window was the main danger point. It was the Jameses' bedroom window when they had no paying guest installed there, when they would move to a smaller room on the second floor. It was a window from which most of our garden and at least part of the conservatory were clearly visible. Mrs James and I had never formed the habit of waving to each other when she was at it and I in the garden, a fact which I hoped she did not attribute solely to me and resent. On the other hand, I did not think that from it she could see anyone unbolting our back gate, walking along Hassell Lane and passing through the Porringers' gate.)

Later, the protagonist having escaped not only her observation but that of Sidney and Julia Colvin (so far as I could see, nobody else's would matter), I should have to represent him as walking back to and along the pier. Aesthetically, it would be best if the novel could end with his descent to the lower deck and down (as I had known since late April) not a ladder but concrete steps to where a boat was waiting to take him back to France.

He had gone to France a week or so before the supposed date of the narrative in order to establish an alibi. His sister, if sister there were, had remained in France.

140

10: Teeth

ALISON AND I were both invited to dinner at the Portsmouth Arms by a cricketing friend whom we had not seen for almost two years. The date proposed was July 10th, a Monday. Accepting, I said that I had recently been having trouble with my teeth and did not know how well I should be able to eat. I fancied that I might have had teeth out by that date. My friend wrote back to say that he, too, had been having trouble and hoped by the 10th to have a new top plate.

When we met in the bar, he began by tapping his new top plate. He also went to Porteous. He had told me before that this was so, but it continued to surprise me. Very successful as a writer, he was not one to have on the National Health anything he could pay for. But it seemed that he knew Porteous outside the surgery, in connection with the school at which his brother had taught. Porteous was a keen fly-fisherman and also given to flying model aeroplanes by radio. The new top plate must have been a bit of a bother to our friend, for he left most of his roast lamb, which looked perfectly tender.

I had put off going and continued to do so for over a month. After breakfast on August 14th (again a Monday), however, I decided to visit Porteous that morning and seek an immediate appointment. My sister (who is better at making appointments than I am) said she would come with me. Accordingly, at a little after nine, she and I walked the short distance up to the end of Clarendon Road (I with

141

my stick), turned a little way left and crossed Jubilee Road into Castle Road, where, at the fourth house, we mounted the steps, rang the bell and pushed the door open, as instructed to by a notice at the side of the door.

The secretary-receptionist came along the passage from the back regions to meet us. She was a stoutly built, rather mannish woman, not unhandsome. My sister remembered her. She had not been on duty when I was there a year and a half before. No doubt she acted as assistant in the surgery when none of the young girls was at hand, they not being early arrivers. From my description of the state of affairs, she decided that my trouble could be classed as an emergency and made me an appointment for 12.15 that midday. Alison and I walked back here, and, while she went out shopping, I settled myself in our back room to pass three apprehensive hours.

These were eventually over. Alison (back from her shopping) and I went back to Porteous's, where we were shown into the waiting room. Of the five other people there, two, a dignified schoolgirl of twelve or so and a middle-aged man, were there for single extractions. Two were the parents of the girl, and, although she was inclined to be chatty, I did not gather anything about the youngish woman, who was in the surgery very briefly and who was not charged anything when she emerged.

The schoolgirl and the middle-aged man went successively to the surgery and then returned to the waiting-room, their gums evidently anaesthetised. I went to the surgery and was given a number of injections, three or four, and returned to the waiting room. The girl and the middle-aged man were called back in turn to the surgery, from which the girl emerged with expressionless dignity, to be taken away by her smiling parents, who were charged some small sum by the secretary-receptionist. The man also came out smiling and assured us that he had not felt a thing.

The time was approaching, was perhaps even past, one

o'clock, and I began to assume that Porteous worked through the lunch hour, perhaps eating a sandwich in some room off the surgery. I was called into the corridor by the girl assistant, who wanted to know whether my gums were thoroughly numb. They weren't. I still had sensation around the two adjacent teeth. The assistant went into the surgery and presently came back to call me in. Porteous gave me a further injection between the adjacent teeth.

He must, I fancy, suddenly have become aware of the time, for, although I was anaesthetised up to the eyes and although nothing had been said earlier about this idea, he then tried to persuade me not to have all four teeth out that day. I rejected the idea, I have since thought mistakenly. I might have accepted it had he suggested pulling out only the backmost tooth that day, but his suggestion was to pull out two teeth. This seemed to me pointless. The backmost tooth was the one I most wanted out. The one I least wanted out was the one on the left. Yet he would presumably go either for this pair or the adjacent teeth, the two most recently anaesthetised. And so I was governed by the feeling that, being once numbed and disliking the sensation or, rather, the lack of it, I ought to go through with the whole process there and then, once and for all.

He started pulling. He pulled the four teeth in rapid succession. When one of the two adjacent teeth was on its way out, I noticed that his forceps were inserted into my mouth quite horizontally. I wondered if they were of a modern kind, whereby, once you had got a grip, the actual pulling was done by the application of some mechanical principle. The late injection had apparently been effective, for I did not much feel those teeth coming out.

After the extractions, Porteous did not waste time telling me when I should next eat or drink anything or what, how much I should wash out my mouth or with what, but almost skittishly, while he was removing his white coat, flung over his shoulder that there had been no breakages. This was because I had confessed earlier that I was a bit

143

nervous of the backmost tooth, with its cavity on the outside, breaking. He then left the surgery.

The secretary-receptionist made me sign two forms. One, I imagine, was to say that four extractions had been made, the other, she told me (for I could not read it without my spectacles), to say that I was not being treated at the moment by any other dentist. While I was paying her in the waiting-room, I saw the stocky form of Porteous marching smartly out of the building, presumably on his way to a delayed lunch. The secretary-receptionist further gave me an appointments card. Although, she said, Mr Porteous might have said that he expected to see me in a week or so, the fact of the matter was that his technician was just off on his holidays, so that the earliest possible appointment for beginning to make dentures would be in three and a half weeks' time.

My sister gave me my stick, and we also left the building, in my case a little shakily. All afternoon, it did not seem to me that I had a lower jaw or, indeed, a bottom lip. At about five o'clock, a little sensation having returned, I managed a cup of lukewarm tea, guiding the cup to my lip with my fingers. Later, I drank a gin-and-tonic without much enjoyment and, later still, a small bowl of soup. So far as I can remember, I slept quite well that night and awoke at a proper time without undue pain, though my jaw certainly ached.

I do not recall what, if anything, I had for breakfast, and my diary does not help me on this point. It does record that the day started clear, but dulled later in the morning. The day before, the day of the extractions, had been dull.

A DIARY ENTRY for August 31st reads:

> After a week's Suzuki music school in Wales, E.J., A. and their children should now be in Brittany, with their boat.
> Of the three and a half weeks before I see Porteous again, two and a half have now elapsed. My jaw still

144

aches, and I am inclined to suspect that at least one root has been left in the socket, though I was assured by Porteous that there had been no breakages.

The last day of August was a Thursday. That Saturday, Betty Hitachi came down from London to see us. While they were away in Brittany, she was staying at the Blacks' in Hampstead. There she returned that evening.

On Monday evening, she telephoned us to say that the Blacks' house had been broken into that afternoon, between the daily help's departure and her own return from wherever she had been. The break-in had evidently been effected by smashing the round ventilator in a basement window and putting an arm through to release the window catch.

The two young academics who lived in the house next door to one side, close friends of Erica Jo's and Angus's, were away. The man next door on the other side had tried to be helpful, putting two screws into the window frame, which would at least serve the purpose of making Betty feel more secure in the house. While she was busy with him and with seeing the police, a new *au pair* girl had arrived, German Swiss and, Betty said, very sweet, a little disconcerted to find herself in a house of which the owners and their children were away and which had just been burgled, if that was the word.

Apart from a clock, Betty had very little idea of what was missing. Erica Jo had not had a great deal of jewellery, and we only hoped that she was wearing her engagement ring, as she had been (Alison had noticed) the last time she was down here.

That Wednesday, my sister went on a history society excursion to Charleston Manor, near Seaford, in the next county, a house of which part dated back to 1080–1100, when it was built on a Saxon site for William the Conqueror's cup bearer, Alured. Its last owner had been Sir Oswald Birley, a portrait painter. Lady Birley, who was very old indeed, helped her girls to show the visitors

145

round. She pointed out the last painting she herself had been able to finish, that of a bunch of garlic. Two women kept the coach waiting, so that Alison was home later than she had expected to be.

Next morning, I went round to Porteous's at a quarter to eleven. He took impressions of my top and bottom jaws separately in horseshoes of warm wax. I gagged while he was doing the top one.

"Breathe deeply," he said, "through the nose only . . . through the nose only . . . through the nose only. . . ."

I did this and stopped gagging. There would be three more visits. The next was to be on Friday, a week and a day later.

Like Lady Birley, my sister was suffering from arthritis. This had started ten or more years ago. A cortisone injection had worked wonders. Latterly, Alison had been having arthritis again. It had been confined to her back, recently also but not at the moment to her feet. It was now extending down her left leg.

I am a selfish man. I was sorry for my sister with her arthritis, but felt that my own dental problem ought to be the only one for the time being. I thought it inconsiderate, if not of my sister to be suffering from arthritis, yet of the arthritis to bother her at the moment. If Alison became crippled, we should be helpless, for I could not walk well enough to do the daily shopping, and few of the local shops delivered.

That Saturday, just before sunset (then at half-past seven), she and I, with a common bravery, took a short walk round the castle, along the sea front and back up Castle Road. As we passed by the side of the Metropole hotel, we saw that working-class youths or boys had at last started breaking windows in the dining-room, while there were squatters, who might be middle-class young, in the first of the ten terrace houses, which belonged to the Metropole.

That weekend, the Blacks returned. Betty's attempted

communication had not reached them, and it was news to them that their house had been broken into. Erica Jo had not been wearing her engagement ring, and so that was gone. I supposed that all petty thieves came from the "working" class, whereas the middle-class young would go in rather for currency swindles and organising bank robberies or pay snatches.

Friday came round again, and I went to Porteous's at 11.45 a.m. His technician was there, in a white coat, a man of proletarian appearance, but entirely dignified and quite silent. He handed Porteous two pieces of a deep pink substance, in which teeth were embedded. Holding these delicately in turn, Porteous proceeded to place them in my open mouth. As he placed the top piece, I started gagging. He began the same rigmarole as before.

"Breathe deeply," he said, "through the nose only . . . through the nose only . . . through the nose only. . . ."

I breathed deeply, through the nose only, and soon stopped gagging, though a little inclined to go on, so as to listen to his incantation, with its two broad Scots *o* sounds at the end. There can be no doubt that the incantation was helpful. I told Porteous that my jaw still ached. He said that we should leave consideration of that fact for the moment.

Next morning, Howard appeared, a good-looking young man of dark colouring, recommended by David Beckford. We had employed him before on smaller jobs and liked him. What he was now to do was repaint the exterior of the whole house and of the sheds, the interior of those parts of the sheds which had been painted before, the gates and the inner side of that part of the six-foot street wall which stood opposite the street-facing part of our front premises and against which grew forsythia, variegated ivy and an enormously spread honeysuckle. These I had already much trimmed.

What he began by doing, with ladders placed here and there, was brush the white paint off the walls with a wire brush. In part, these walls had a surface which I had called

147

pebbledashed. This was not the right word, but I have forgotten what the right word was. Although it was Saturday, Howard worked all day, going home for lunch and returning early in the afternoon, when he worked on until after six o'clock.

MY PENULTIMATE VISIT to Porteous was on Wednesday, the 20th of September, at 3.45 p.m., a time of day at which I should have preferred to be rising from my afternoon rest to a cup of my sister's well-made tea. My luncheon that day, like all my meals for over five weeks past, had consisted of fairly soft food, as I had been without teeth.

The technician was in attendance again. We greeted each other, and he produced teeth embedded in what looked like the same pieces of rosy pink substance, so that I began to wonder if my false teeth would always have false gum of that rather startling colour, instead of the pale pink I had come to think of as customary.

Porteous fitted them in and began to intone: "Breathe deeply, through the nose only, through the. . . ."

But I was beginning to learn to gag only once or twice.

The girl brought a mirror, and Porteous asked me whether the appearance of the teeth suited me. I suggested that the two middle bottom teeth might be reduced somewhat, as, when I had had my own teeth, the bottom ones had rarely shown. As a matter of fact, I considered that the whole bottom lot sloped upward to the right, and wondered if, on the one hand, my bottom lip might still be sloping a little downward towards the right, two years after my stroke, and if, on the other, my gums might still be more swollen on the right and would subside. Besides, the poor technician would have a terrible job filing down all the right-hand bottom teeth or whatever he would have to do to correct the slope. So I said nothing about that matter, for the moment.

I reminded Porteous, however, of what seemed to me a matter of greater consequence, *viz.*, that, five weeks after

148

the extractions, my jaw was still aching and that, after the first fortnight, the ache had grown somewhat worse. He talked of X-rays and of seeing a consultant, but considered that we should wait until I had worn my dentures for a while, during which time I should take Veganin twice a day.

In order that, on Friday, I should be able to take him a cheque ready made out, I looked at Porteous's plate on the way out, to see what his initials were.

On Friday afternoon, Porteous did take X-rays. If anything untoward was visible, he did not tell me. The false gum had acquired a pale pink. The teeth were put in place with almost no gagging and so no incantation. Their proud wearer, I walked out of the surgery and, in the waiting-room, gave the secretary-receptionist my cheque for £20, with a little extra in cash for the X-rays. I signed another form.

The teeth seemed enormous. I could not imagine how the least morsel of food got in between them. Every now and then, I had a fit of gagging, upon which I breathed deeply through the nose only. I also did, as instructed, a lot of swallowing. Porteous had not told me whether he favoured keeping the dentures in at night. For cleaning, he had recommended a nail brush and ordinary toilet soap.

I had some difficulty in lighting cigarettes and did not draw on them easily. I drank tea with some pleasure, but, when I moved on to gin-and-tonic, I did not seem to be tasting it fully. The bubbles reached my palate (at the top, I had had what Bone called a half-plate, which left my palate uncovered), but I had, I felt sure, formerly tasted them with the edges of my gums, now shut off by pink plastic.

The first thing I ate was a small, salty Ritz biscuit, which gave me no pleasure, though I had been missing those particular biscuits for the past five and a half weeks. My front teeth would, indeed, break the biscuit into pieces, but would not grind the pieces into a paste, as three of the teeth I had had six weeks before would.

149

Next, I ate plaice and chips, with a small quantity of beer. I put some of the chips into sandwiches of thinly cut brown bread and butter, from which the crust had been removed. I managed the bits of fried plaice, but the chip sandwiches and the chips I put into my mouth by themselves would only chew up into a mess which dislodged both top and bottom dental plates, so that, with my gums, I was chewing a mixture of bread, chips and teeth.

With the help of my tongue, I managed a mouthful or two. I then took my dentures to the kitchen sink, rinsed them, placed them on the draining-board and returned to table toothless.

I might, I said, wear them socially, for cosmetic reasons, but I could not eat with them. Alison told me what one of her shopping friends had said, upon being informed that I was visiting a dentist to have false teeth fitted.

"Oh," the woman had said, "my old father always used to take his out to eat."

I thought that a good story. It seemed likely to be the case with me.

To go to bed, I nevertheless put the bottom plate in. I feared that it might be uncomfortable on the side of my face I had down to the pillow, but there was no discomfort, despite the fact that it was with the right side of my face to the pillow that I settled down to sleep and that latterly I had experienced much discomfort when sleeping or attempting to sleep without denture. (I am convinced, I may say, that I continue sleeping in one position unless I wake and deliberately turn over, despite the view of scientific observers that people turn over constantly in their sleep, as perhaps they do when a scientific observer is in the room, despite also the fact that my wife had characterised me as a particularly restless sleeper, so that in the end we had stopped trying to sleep in the same bed.) I slept until almost half-past five, which was longer than I had been sleeping lately. When I awoke, I turned over. As soon as the left side of my face touched the pillow, my bottom denture

150

sprang out of place. Luckily, I was able to take it out and drop it into the blue plastic mug on my bedside table, which already contained the top plate in water.

I was still thinking about the implications of the evident fact that my bottom plate did not fit on the left when I heard what sounded like a kettle boiling below. My sister, up early, and wishing to make herself a pot of tea, seemed to be letting it boil too hard and too long. I wondered whether it was boiling dry and whether I ought to get up and see to it. Then it became much louder and was, I felt sure, a sound from outside the house. I got up.

Alison was, indeed, up and had intended making tea, but when she had filled the kettle, she had found it impossible to turn the tap off. The cold tap in the kitchen was running full pelt and could not be turned off.

It was too early to ring up a plumber, and the water board was in Hastings. We decided to ring up Mr Burgess, a plumber we knew and liked, at seven o'clock, in about an hour's time. My sister located the mains tap and turned that off as hard as she could. I turned a bit harder. The tap did not stop running, but its flow diminished. The plumber came at about half-past eight, found a split washer, replaced it and charged us 80 pence.

HOWARD FINISHED WHAT we call the front of the house and knocked off work to spend the rest of the weekend with his wife and children. When my sister came home with her weekend shopping, it included a tube of Steradent tablets, an oddly shaped container of Kolynos powder and a selection of small brushes for me to choose from.

Very nice the front of the house looked. The house wall was white, as before, and so was the inner side of the six-foot wall which, except for a wrought-iron gate and a bow window, secludes us from Clarendon Road. Howard had taken endless trouble with the glossy white paint round the sixty small panes of the bow window. The door, the gutters and the drain pipes were an intense blue-green known as Channel blue, which we greatly preferred to the pale blue which had been there before. We had thought of other colours, but, as soon as Howard had suggested Channel blue, we had liked it. The weather had been perfect for painting all week, though twice it had looked as if it were going to rain and had in fact rained heavily for a minute or two the previous Sunday evening.

That Saturday evening, Alison went with Joy to a recital at the Pavilion by John Georgiadis, leader of the London Symphony Orchestra, and his wife. I put in my teeth and very satisfactorily got through a bowl of lovage soup in which a stale crust had been broken up. Also with them in, I ate a scone containing sultanas.

Next day at midday came a real test, the Sunday joint, a shoulder of lamb with roast potatoes and a cauliflower, followed by chocolates. I survived this with credit, though my sister had finished her main course long before I had, and mine went cold. My slowness was due to my mouthfuls being very small and to the fact that the teeth fitted loosely. Bits of food would get beneath them, and they would become dislodged when I bit into, for instance, a substantial piece of meat or roast potato or an unusually large piece of cauliflower. I also frequently bit my tongue, more painfully than with real teeth. The chocolates presented their own problems, seeming hard on the outside and peculiarly sticky inside and, as I should discover when I went into the cloakroom afterwards to rinse my teeth and brush them with the brush I had selected, leaving a fair amount of dark brown substance in the crevices between the separate teeth. It was no doubt for cosmetic reasons that the teeth were planted separately, even at the back, where a continuous plastic might have seemed preferable, though perhaps disclosed by a very wide yawn. One understood that Russians generally had false teeth made of metal.

IN THE LAST week of September, the weather was poor. Monday was dull, as indeed, Sunday had been. There was rain in the late afternoon on Tuesday, though it cleared, so that at six o'clock my sister and I walked along the sea front to the Lord Sidmouth.

Wednesday started damp, and there were further showers just after midday and again at four o'clock in the afternoon. Thursday was thoroughly wet. Howard did not appear on Wednesday afternoon or on Thursday morning. On Thursday afternoon, he was able to occupy himself with clearing mud from the gutter inside one of the two sheds and with white-painting parts of the interiors of both sheds and the inside of the door on the one which has a door.

Friday turned cold, and we put the central heating on low. It had started damp, with a bit of a shower at 1.20 p.m. Howard came late that morning, but then started work on the north side of the house, the side facing the Porringers'. He needed a tall ladder to the eaves. Our path up that side of the house being very narrow and on a bit of a slope, he felt that he needed to plant his ladder on the Porringers' side of the garden wall, or the ladder would be almost vertical, with a north-west wind blowing up. This was clearly the unwelcome moment at which I needed to go round and up to their back door and arrange matters with whoever was there, I hoped Mrs Porringer.

While I was indoors making myself presentable, Fagg came out and Howard himself asked his permission to plant his ladder on the other side of the wall. Fagg said he couldn't. Howard and I discussed this. He said that he understood that in such situations a neighbour was compelled to give ground, but that he would not press the point. If necessary, he would get a brother of his round to hold the ladder. I volunteered myself to hold the ladder, but he did not seem to think this a good idea, whether from the point of view of customer-workman relations or because he had noticed signs of my infirmity and did not think that I should be good at holding ladders. In the end, he planted his ladder as well as he could and got up it.

This, I think, was the moment at which I first began to think of the plot of my novel as a possible scenario for action, though Fagg would then have to become the first victim, instead of an innocent though suspected bystander. In order to disoblige me, he had been willing to put a fellow workman in peril of a serious accident. This was utterly evil, and Mrs James's regard for Fagg could not mitigate it. Howard, I may say, had, as he told me, already had an accident as the result of a ladder falling.

The following morning, it was colder still, and we turned the heating on full. That was Saturday, the last day of September, with a strong wind from the north-west. Howard came late that morning, but was soon up his almost vertical ladder, without brother. The Porringers' garden was full of girls, no doubt there because he was so good-looking. Afterwards, he said to me that he would not have liked his own children to talk to each other the way those did. I did not find an opportunity of asking him in just what way they had been talking to each other, whether, for instance, it had been indecent.

Two newspaper cuttings are here tucked into my diary. One is from the local paper. It shows six Morris dancers, four of them bearded, performing, in their curious costumes, at the pier entrance (they were to perform later on the green outside the Lord Sidmouth). Alison in the course of her shopping did not see them. *A fortiori*, neither did I. Nor did she or I see anything of the behaviour of migrant swallows which, for the second time that year, got this town into the national news next day.

Under the heading

Birds try
to invade
houses

the nature correspondent of my Sunday newspaper reported:

> THOUSANDS of young swallows on migration, robbed of insect food by the cold snap and bewildered by the high winds, became frenzied, . . . flinging themselves against windows in attempts to get into houses and then collapsing on roads in front of cars.
>
> Birdwatchers . . . reported flights of immature swallows behaving in a similarly demented manner, some killing themselves by trying to fly into woodland thickets in search of insects.
>
> Mr David Butterworth, a motorist of London Road, . . . said: "The birds appeared to be intent upon suicide. They just dropped right in front of the lines of moving vehicles."
>
> The swallows also swept low over parties of anglers anchored in open boats. . . . Mr Ted Irwin, of Bromley Road, Catford, said after coming ashore: "The swallows kept diving on the boats. It was quite unnerving."
>
> Mr James Cadbury, head of the Royal Society for the Protection of Birds' scientific research department at Cambridge, said there was a similar incident three years ago on the northern slopes of the Alps when starving swallows trying to reach the Mediterranean threw themselves against buildings and thousands died on the roads.

There was rain again on Sunday, but Monday was quite a good day. Howard finished work on the house.

In the larger seaside town of Blackpool, two hundred miles north of here and a little to the west, the Labour Party's annual conference opened. In the hope of curbing the devaluation of our currency, a Labour prime minister proposed that demands for annual pay increases should that year be limited to 5 per cent. His proposal was rejected by a majority of more than two to one, principally effected

155

by a showing of cards held by the general secretaries of two trade unions, the Amalgamated Engineers' and the Transport and General Workers', and held to represent the views of their two million members. Those views had not been solicited.

Not that there is in general much point in soliciting the views of members of the "working" class, who will normally go along with their unions in demanding as much as possible. I was learning to distinguish, however, between the "working" class proper and those of working-class culture, as it is sometimes called, who are self-employed and cannot go on strike, whose incomes are directly related to the amount of work they do. There were examples before my eyes.

Howard could not go on strike, nor could Mr Burgess, the plumber. Fagg could not have gone on strike in his capacity as a driving instructor, but would have to as a maintenance man at the mines, might indeed have gone on strike with other maintenance men on behalf of what were called their differentials.

AT OUR LARGEST car factories, the "workers" were already on strike while the Labour Party conference proceeded. So they were at certain hospitals. They all continued to take this form of industrial inaction in the second week of October, while the Conservative Party was holding its annual conference at another large seaside town, Brighton, nearer here, with speeches both for and against compulsory wage restraint and in favour of capital punishment. Elsewhere, there was much agitation against a proposed seal cull in the Orkneys, these vermin being larger than most and found in romantic places.

A British punk rock star was accused in New York of murdering his American girlfriend. A Securicor guard was shot dead in London during a pay snatch.

The weather deteriorated during the third week of October. Crude oil was pouring from a Greek tanker off the coast of Pembrokeshire. In Rome, a new pope was announced, for a change a Pole.

In my wallet, I discovered a little brochure, which must have been given me by Porteous's secretary-receptionist when I paid her for my false teeth and the X-rays. Perhaps because it was the last thing to offer me reassurance about my teeth, I have remained fond of this little brochure and kept it for almost a year under a scribbling pad on the stripped-pine mantelpiece of the ornamental fireplace in the downstairs back room where I now am. It is called *Your New Dentures* and published by the manufacturers of Kolynos.

On its first page, it says:

IMPORTANT WARNING

On no account must you immerse or wash acrylic (plastic) dentures in very hot or boiling water. This will warp the dentures and ruin the fit. Use only cold or lukewarm water for cleaning or rinsing.

When not in use acrylic dentures should be kept in cold water.

This was not particularly reassuring when I first read it. The instructions on my tube of Steradent tablets recommended placing the dentures in water "as hot as the finger can bear" and only then dropping in one of the effervescent tablets. I had followed this procedure more than once. So far as I could see or feel, I did not think that I had thereby warped the dentures and ruined the fit, though I did wonder if the edges of individual teeth had been roughened.

More or less prolonged steeping in a solution of Steradent cleans false teeth. Kolynos is a fine powder to be sprinkled in the pink grooves on the gum side of the teeth. In contact with saliva, it becomes sticky and constitutes a fixative, giving the wearer confidence that his false teeth will not jump out of his mouth while he is speaking, perhaps even permitting him the wide, impolitely uncovered yawn. I had not yet experimented with Kolynos, but was presently to do so on a social occasion and to be filled with confidence, though still somewhat inhibited in my conversation and in eating the various *canapés* offered.

My jaw still ached. It was worse on Tuesday, October 17th. I was in a state of confusion about this ache. I was in a state of confusion about my teeth. I was also in a neurotic state. This had much to do with my feelings about Porteous, whether I felt that I could trust him, for instance. He had a good reputation. Dr Millard had said that he was a wonderful dentist, though she did not herself go to him. Mrs Nicholson had found him all that could be desired.

A piece of what I can only think misinformation from Mrs Nicholson was one thing that was misleading me. She had apparently regarded a first set of teeth as temporary and had gone back some months later, three months I think, to be fitted for a permanent set. Alison also had twice been sent appointments cards for check-ups, but did not tell me that for both these cards she had paid the secretary-receptionist for stamps. And so I was vainly waiting to be summoned by Porteous, who indeed had said nothing about seeing me again, though he had invited me to make appointments if I found my teeth did not fit.

I was wearing them very rarely and had found they rubbed in one place on the only occasion when I had worn them for two meals running. I was also not taking Veganin twice a day, being nervous of any drug containing aspirin. Porteous had not, in any case, said for how long I should go on taking Veganin, in the hope, presumably, that it would sooner or later stop the ache in my jaw.

The ache was at its worst when I was in bed, with my head on a pillow. It arose equally in the three places where I had had teeth extracted, but was worse in those on the right. It seemed unlikely that Porteous should have left pieces of root in all three places (I was counting the two adjacent teeth as one place). The pain was inward. It was definitely my jaw which ached, not my gums, in which there was no sign of infection and which, indeed, were never happier than when chewing the crustless sandwiches of cold meat and salad, the grated apple and cheese, often with pastry, which constituted my lunches. The effect was as if I still had my teeth and they were aching. Alison thought there must be abscesses, but it seemed unlikely similarly that abscesses should form in all three places. An entry in *Pear's Medical Encyclopaedia* said that neuritis sometimes develops after the extraction of teeth, and I tried to believe in neuritis, but did not think it would behave in quite that way.

I wondered about the consultant, to whom Porteous would no doubt send me. My objection to seeing a consultant was that it would almost certainly mean travelling to the nearest large hospital, and, my legs being as they were, I could not face the difficulty, with walks through railway stations, from bus stops and along hospital corridors, there being obviously no possibility of being taken there by ambulance for a dental matter. The hospital situation was, moreover, not good at the time.

Maintenance men were striking more widely, and patients in a dangerous condition could not be admitted. By the third Friday in October, five hospitals in the country had been closed, and more than a hundred others had been reduced to admitting emergencies only. The strike was of the type known as a go-slow, so that the strikers were still being paid. They were striking over differentials, being, that is to say, of the opinion that they were not being paid enough more than the engineers who worked under them. The opinion of consultant physicians and surgeons was that people had already died and that others would never recover as a result of this form of industrial action (or inaction).

The cars having got there unblacked, the annual motor show opened on Saturday, not at Earls Court, but for the

159

first time in Birmingham, where it was less of a traffic nuisance. The amount of theft and damage was, however, greater even than would have been expected in London.

At Dunstable in Hertfordshire, a shock awaited the leaders of no fewer than five unions when, at the beginning of the last full week in October, they had addressed a mass meeting of Vauxhall car workers. These men voted not to go on strike. "This is terrible!" said the Transport and General representative. At a larger mass meeting of Vauxhall car workers in the neighbouring town of Luton next day, the same astonishing vote was recorded.

There must be a catch in it somewhere, but clearly exceptions may be found to my thought of a moment ago that it is in general futile to solicit the views of the "working" class. The workers of Hertfordshire were perhaps behind the times, or something had kept the younger "workers" away from those mass meetings, while their elders had turned up in force. These facts about life in the great outside world I discover from a pile of copies of the *Daily Mail* which has accumulated over a period of almost a year in the crime room, I don't quite know why, though it probably had to do with another novel I planned. The collection of papers ends on September. I may continue to refer to them in the time that remains.

11: Interlude

IT WAS STILL the open season for noise from next door. On the last day of October, a Tuesday, on half-term holiday, Porringer suddenly appeared with a cement-mixer, these machines having presumably been packed up for the winter by those who normally used them. The chief object, it presently transpired, was a final cementing of the floor of the chicken-wired carport, where we supposed a garage was finally to be built. The machine, however, was installed on the grass patch or lawn opposite our kitchen window, the cement being carried to the carport in buckets. The first machine apparently not working well, Fagg and Porringer were both to be seen and heard on Friday, November 3rd, busy cementing with a second machine.

The bakers were on strike, and next day there was not a loaf of bread to be found in the town, working-class wives having bought it all up to store in their deep freezes. That evening, there were a bit of a bonfire and fireworks next door, although it was the 4th and not the 5th of the month. This seemed a curious exhibition of latent sabbatarianism.

I was suffering from unusual headaches which curiously seemed to be brought on by coughing. Reluctant as I was to bother him (or to sit in his waiting room for half an hour or more and then be admitted for five minutes' hurried consultation), I went round the corner to see Dr Roper. With the utmost expedition, I mentioned the headaches, my legs and my jaw. The headaches were child's play. That was sinuses, and pills were prescribed (they were not to prove at all helpful). As to my legs, he made me take my shoes and socks off and felt both calves. He could, he said, feel a pulsation in the one, but not in the other. He could do nothing about it. As to my jaw, he didn't know the answer to that one.

I wondered if he had taken a dislike to me. I had not bothered him, and he was always very good with my sister. It was an unsatisfactory visit.

Wednesday of that week, the second full week of November, was four weeks after my third visit from the police, provoked on that occasion by myself. On a Wednesday morning, four weeks before, I had seen in the garden a long piece of wood, presumably tossed over the street wall after dark last evening. It was a quarter round in section and from twelve to fifteen feet in length. As it was new wood and had presumably been stolen, if only from a building site, by the individual who tossed it over, I had rung up the police about it at midday, rather apologetically. A young policeman with a moustache had called at nine o'clock in the evening. He had examined the piece of wood, called it quadrant, written out a report in which he said I should be keeping the length of quadrant and told me that I should keep it for a month, in case anybody claimed it.

Four weeks to the day, I sawed it up into three pieces and put them in the nearer shed, the one with the door. It would have gone into the shed in two pieces. I sawed it up for no better reason that that I felt, the month being up,, that I should do something with it, having grown tired of seeing it lying out on the concrete.

About the futility of my occupations at this time, I could add a further detail connected with the same incident. It had also to do with life in general under the government of the day, which was busy reorganising the country into entities of a different size and shape, here and there ignoring county boundaries and, for instance, making a present of Monmouthshire to Wales. This county remained largely intact, but our town was incorporated in a district area centred upon the neighbouring seaport. We still had a police station of our own (I did not know where it was), but it had no telephone number. Telephoning in the first place about my length of quadrant, I had rung police in the seaport, mainly, I feel sure, to find out what then happened, whether, that is to say, one had to report to the seaport police, who then activated the local police, or whether the seaport police put one through to the local station. This they had done. That was what they did.

Futile also was my behaviour when Dr Roper had to visit this house very shortly after my visit to him. No sooner had I paid this than I had developed a pain in the upper part of my chest, which I might have suspected to be the sign of a recurrence of coronary thrombosis but for the fact that it did not go right across but was confined to the left side. My sister taking to bed with a temperature, Roper came round and diagnosed 'flu. As he was about to depart, I asked him whether he had time also to take a look at me. "No," he said, but then, "What is it?" I told him about my chest. He made me remove my pullover, shirt and singlet, put his stethoscope where I told him the pain was and pronounced it clear. "Well," said I, "the pain is certainly there. What could it be?" "It could be a tumour," said he, "in which case you'd be coughing blood or losing weight. You'd better have an X-ray." He started making out a card. "No," said I, and he, "Why? Are you afraid of what they'd find?" "It isn't that," I said, "but I'm neither losing weight nor coughing blood." "Well," he said, "I've done two patients in one visit." And he went. My objection was in fact simply to the bother and fatigue of a visit to the local hospital for an X-ray. I could have got a taxi there, but not back. I had mentioned my jaw again, but he just laughed.

For the rest of the year, nothing much happened in my world. Three times, I was in great pain between four and five o'clock in the morning, with a combination of chest and jaw, but by six it was passing off. Mr Owen died. My sister went to his funeral service at St Peter's. An old lady across the road also died, and her husband came over to tell us that she had done so. Neither of us had ever met her, though we knew him, having greatly admired the sweet peas he grew against a north wall. The walls and windows of the drill hall in which the RAF cadets met to practise drumming were daubed and sprayed with yellow paint.

Radio tunings changed. They changed on the fourth day of the proceedings at Minehead against Jeremy Thorpe and others. This was sufficiently in my world for Alison and me to listen to the news on the wireless, usually at six o'clock in the evening, for over three weeks until the hearings were over on December 13th. To my mind, although the proceedings might have had to be taken, most of the evidence that was heard should have been disallowed, as it was quite irrelevant to the charges. Neither did it seem to me that there was any *prima facie* case to go forward.

The trade-union war against hospital patients continued, and Christmas television was threatened. The IRA bombed Christmas shoppers and machine-gunned guardsmen. As Iranian oil dried up, a petrol strike seemed likely here. Hugh Scanlon was made a life peer on his retirement from striking.

THE NEW YEAR began with snow, which in the first place went on until January 7th. There was further snow in the evening of the 10th, which persisted with a terrible wind from the north-west next day and was then gone. We had snow again on the 19th, with an east wind, and this lasted, with a rainy interval, till the 25th. It came again on the 29th, but mixed with hail, sleet and rain, which finally, for the time being, conquered, though more snow was to fall on February 14th and to remain for a week.

There were new strikes, of course. The first I noted was that of lorry drivers, which began on the first day without snow. Denise and her intermittent Clarendon Road friend

164

were out at the back. The next day, their school term started. The day after that, I saw a chaffinch in the garden. In next day's briefer snow, wartime mines which had been discovered were detonated somewhere along the coast. I heard five out of fifteen. That Saturday, I saw a pair of chaffinches. Dr Henderson had had his heart attack and was in intensive care in the county town.

On the 18th, buses and trains were on strike. Porringer's car would not start, and the children were at home for two days, including Jeremy. On the second of these two days, they were all put out, well wrapped up, the baby included. They erected a bit of a snow man and threw thawing snow at each other. Jeremy did most of the shrieking.

The Faggs or Porringers had put up a tray on the piece of piping which had formerly held the whirligig clothes-drier. On this they placed enormous crusts of stale bread and other kitchen refuse. On this clouds of starlings descended. These were birds not often seen in our garden, and I found them singularly repulsive at close quarters. This, I suppose, was largely because they walked instead of hopping. Even female blackbirds hopped. The starlings waddled, disputing crusts they had brought over. I frequently opened the outer conservatory doors to scare them away.

I did this after lunch on Friday, the 26th of January. As one of the starlings had dropped a crust on the concrete, I picked it up and threw it back over the garden wall. Fagg was at home. He came down their path on the other side of the wall, murmuring unintelligibly.

"What do you say?" I asked him in dulcet tones, determined to be friendly.

He spoke more distinctly, though still quietly.

"Do you mind," he said, "not throwing things into our garden?"

"Oh," said I jovially, "if bread comes over, we shall throw it back."

At that moment, my sister appeared at the conservatory door.

165

"We don't want your dry bread in our garden," she said. "It encourages vermin."

Fagg turned and walked back up their path and the two steps to the porch door. The effect was that of slinking away.

Alsion was sure that his wife had sent him. My sister does not usually drink anything at midday during the week. Her intake of alcohol is very modest indeed, consisting as a rule of one small martini or sherry before dinner, a little white wine with the superior fish on Tuesday, half a glass of beer with the coarse fish on Friday, a martini at midday on Saturday and the same on Sunday, plus red wine with the joint for Sunday lunch, which is our principal meal in the week.

That Friday, however, she was a wee bit tiddly in the early afternoon, having perhaps had a glass of sherry with one of her shopping friends and then another on her return home. When we discussed the incident afterwards, she admitted having come to the conservatory door with aggressive intent and not merely to shake the tablecloth.

Of what were to be this year's principal nuisances, one could be held to have started next day, Saturday. In the afternoon, the two small boys, a year or so younger than himself, who lived next door to each other in Clarendon Road, arrived to play with Jeremy on the grass patch or lawn outside our kitchen window. They were to be rained off for the next three weeks, but would thereafter be constantly around.

I have no note of the dates of the funeral attendants' strike, and newspapers are missing, but it was at about this time. For a while, the dead were going unburied. It was not as bad as it would have been in summer, unlike most of the strikes that were going on.

A snowdrop was out in the garden on February 7th. On the 8th, a murder was discovered in the south part of the town.

It had been decreed by some world organisation to be

the International Year of the Child. To this I propose to make my own contribution, but it does not seem to me that, seven months later, anyone else has paid much attention to this fact, except the designers of postage stamps. It may, in some obscure way, account for the number of perambulators and push-chairs the working-class women from lower down Clarendon Road, most of them looking disgruntled, may now be seen pushing past our wrought-iron gate. The older children are, I would say, no better provided than they have been for some years past with balls, bicycles, new clothes, sweets and spending money. In general, they are nasty, and there are too many of them in this overpopulated country. Most of them ought never to have been born.

THE FIRST NOTE on the year's second nuisance does not occur until April 14th, a Saturday, eve of Easter. Forsythia, squills and hyacinths were out. The IRA had killed Airey Neave. The Metropole hotel had been sold to Arabs, who seemed to have no distinct idea what they were going to do with it and had found it in worse condition than they expected.

As to the nuisance, the only note I have is "antique dealer's kid next door, p.m." There is no indication of what nuisance he may have committed that afternoon, possibly none except to be there. Fair-haired, the youngest of his family, with older sisters, he was rather a pretty boy with a twisted mouth and a loud voice. He was an exhibitionist, one recurrent manifestation of which fact was a kind of tribal dance he would perform, stamping around with his arms in the air.

No doubt the Clarendon Road boys were there as well, for the following day I note with astonishment that there were "*no* children evening. A. at church." That day had started with the foghorn blowing and turned out quite hot. The Blacks were around, and Angus had fetched us for Sunday luncheon. My jaw was bad.

A vote of confidence having gone against them on March 28th, the Labour government was out, and elections pended. On Monday, April 16th, Angus Black brought stable manure from the riding school his children attended when they were down here. We had tickets for a meeting that evening at the Pavilion, to be addressed by Lord Carrington on behalf of the local Conservative candidate. Angus stayed and went with us. Among the people we knew there was Porteous, the dentist. There was no heckling. We came out at question time, the questions asked by local Conservatives being singularly futile.

The children next door, the girls at any rate, must have been away part of that week, for on Thursday the Whistler and Denise are reported as "back, a.m." They were very noisy on Saturday afternoon. A thrush's nest, in cotoneaster at the front, had been deserted. It contained three cold, white eggs, one damaged. I had a bonfire. My chest and jaw were bad. The following week was wet. The elections took place on May 3rd. There was frost that weekend, but then the weather picked up. The white, perennial candytuft was out. The aubretia was past its best. Sunday, May 13th, was suddenly bright and hot. The children next door were out in force. They included the antique dealer's son.

The heat continuing (with some diminution after two days), I turned the central heating off next day. The girls next door appeared in bathing costumes at the back. There was no reason why they shouldn't, but next door's summer campaign against us had, I felt, opened.

This was to take an odd form. The essential strategy was an evident decree by Mrs Fagg that the baby (as I still call it, though it is now a toddler rising three and able to speak incoherently, its name constantly escaping me) had to be out on the grass patch whenever it was fine. One of the older children had to be with it, because of a tendency it displayed to stray into dangerous situations, either out into Hassell Lane or up stacked wood on to the doctors'

168

wall. At first, Denise had taken her turn at this duty, but soon it devolved wholly upon Jeremy, who, outside school hours, was virtually a prisoner in the garden, into which had to come whatever small boys wished to play with him or found the grass patch more commodious than any facilities they were allowed to use at home. In the past, Fagg had often barked at visiting boys or sent them away, but was latterly more often out all evening and, when here, exhibited a silent tolerance, as Porringer had always done, the women never appearing. The girls came in or out and stimulated the boys to frenzies of excitement, making the baby scream.

The play was neither traditional nor inventive. The only traditional game I ever saw played next door was that in which one child hides its face and the others creep up on him or her, the one child suddenly turning and pointing at any it sees in movement, who must thereafter take its place. This game had, I imagine, been set up by Marianne James, who played with Jeremy and the baby (and whatever visitors Jeremy had) more often than did either of his sisters, who often seemed not to want her. I can only guess where she had learnt it, for traditional children's games seem to have been generally forgotten. They no longer have whips and tops or the kind of hoops you bowl along, wooden ones with a stick, iron ones (for boys only) with an iron handle ending in a crook. Nowadays, without a ball or a bicycle, all children seem to do is run about shrieking. They have, I fancy, fewer fights than we did. Our fighting, however, consisted either of fair fisticuffs or, more often, of simple wrestling, in which one boy attempted to get another flat on his back on the ground and admit defeat. Nowadays, except as a spectator sport between professional boxers, weaponless fisticuffs no longer appeal to the young, who, if one got another down, would bang his head on the pavement or "put in the boot". Boys therefore wisely avoid such dangerous encounters.

169

ON SATURDAY, MAY 19th, towards noon, I answered the doorbell, and to my surprise there stood Fagg. He explained himself quite intelligibly. Timothy's ball had not been thrown or knocked over the garden wall by other boys, but dropped there by the child himself. Could he have it back?

"I will put it back," I said.

I can't remember whether Fagg thanked me, but he in some way signified contentment and prepared to withdraw. As his manner was not unfriendly, I asked him whether he could stop the children making so much noise outside our kitchen window. To this he answered that he was usually out.

"There are other people in the house, aren't there?" I said.

"Yes," said he. Then he volunteered: "It will be different when we get the wall built."

"What wall?"

"Oh, we're making a wall across the garden," he said.

He went, carefully shutting the gate behind him. Presently, I went round the north of our house and picked up from the path a sizeable ball with a coloured pattern. A number of boys were sitting quietly on the grass. They included the antique dealer's son, to whom my sister always referred as the Horror (to be more specific, I had tried calling him the Antique, but this name had never caught on). He stood up and made as if to take the ball from me, but I threw it to the feet of Timothy, who was wandering aimlessly about. He looked at me, but paid no attention to the ball.

"Say thank you!" exclaimed Jeremy, as one whose job it was to inculcate politeness in his juniors.

The child, of course, said nothing, but looked blankly at the stranger over the wall. I came indoors, thinking hopefully that an era of better relations had perhaps dawned between ourselves and the Faggs, Porringers and Lamberts.

It was a bright day, though cold. In the afternoon, Fagg and Porringer were mixing cement, and Porringer was busy with something at the far end of their concrete path to the gate. Later in the afternoon, from my bedroom window, I saw a sight I had never expected to see (and have not seen since). This was of Grandma (Mrs Porringer) and the Whistler (Angela) playing pat-ball with tennis rackets along Hassell Lane. I call it pat-ball rather than tennis because it was gentler, though what Denise and her friends played either there or in the doctors' was not tennis either, but simply a form of slam-ball, without rules or marked lines and clearly useless as practice if ever Denise started playing tennis at school or elsewhere, as I should have thought she might have done at one of the local clubs or on the courts in Alexandra Park.

In the morning, I found a pale-green tennis ball on the flowerbed to the right, against the dividing wall. In the interest of better relations, I tossed it over and then stood on the low parapet to see where it had fallen. It had fallen into a ditch which, unseen by me, Porringer had dug just beyond the concrete path for five years or so, after which it began to turn away from the path. In the ditch were bricks already laid as though to provide the foundations of a wall.

ON TUESDAY EVENING, a bigger boy joined those next door. He came with the antique dealer's son and was, I supposed, his elder brother (the two being similarly dressed in green blazers, the bigger in long trousers) and thus an older son of the antique dealer, whose name, I think, we already knew to be Prior and who lived in Jubilee Road next door to an unmarried woman friend of ours, to whom he was a nuisance by reason of the smell from his bonfires, on which he no doubt burned varnished wood and whose smoke would, in the prevailing wind (even here, from the south-west), blow across her garden and into her back premises. This big boy had a white ball, patterned with the usual black hexagons, which, if it was not full match weight, was certainly full match size.

With this ball, five or even six boys began to play football on the small grass patch outside our kitchen window and, indeed, two other windows. If it did not break a window, it was bound, sooner or later, to come over the garden wall. It did. Alison went out to look. The big boy was about to come over after his ball, but, seeing her and seeing that she saw him, drew back. All the boys withdrew. I went round, picked up the ball and took it along the concrete behind the house and down the path to the gate, where I placed it by the dustbin.

A little while later, the doorbell rang. My sister answered it. There stood three boys, the big one, the Horror and the friendly electrician's son. The big boy asked for his ball. Alison was angry. She asked the three whether they would be allowed to play football like that in their own gardens.

It was the antique dealer's known son, the Horror, who, to his credit, answered: "No."

I fancy I also must have gone briefly to the door, for I have a distinct visual image of the boys standing there. I left the talking, however, to my angry sister. She told them they could not have the ball. They went, and we are both under the impression that they closed the gate behind them.

Some while afterwards, when dusk had begun to fall, the doorbell rang again. Alison went. There stood the big boy with his father, who asked unceremoniously for his son's ball.

This time, my sister came into the back room, where I was sitting, and told me that a bearded man stood at the door and that she thought I had better deal with him. It was not, she said, the antique dealer. For whatever reason, I persisted in half believing that it was, knowing that the antique dealer (whom I had never seen) was bearded, supposing that Alison had only briefly had him pointed out to her and this man having with him a boy whom I

172

supposed to be a son of the antique dealer. I went to the door.

I asked the man what his name was.

"Why?" he asked.

"I don't like talking to people whose names I don't know." I said.

"What's yours?" he countered.

"I'll know yours first," said I.

He would not tell me his name, though I cannot remember in what form he refused or what he then said.

"Are you," I went on, "the antique dealer who lives in Jubilee Road?"

"No, I'm not," said he, exasperated.

"Where *do* you live?" I asked him.

To this he must have answered distinctly that he was not going to tell me where he lived, for I said: "Bugger off, then."

"Oh, charming!" said he.

A middle-class usage, I thought. But I was already closing the door. He pushed at it, but either I used more strength, or he gave up. The gate stood open. I had to open the door again and go out to shut the gate.

We discussed what to do with the ball. Alison was against putting it in the dustbin, though there was room for it and next day was the day for the dustmen. In the morning, we had further discussion. My sister's opposition to putting the ball in the dustbin was unemphatic, and so, when I went round to unbolt the gate, I put the ball in the dustbin under garden refuse. The dustmen came at half-past eight or a quarter to nine, and one of them tipped it into their cart.

At about eleven o'clock, while Alison was out shopping and drinking coffee, I answered the doorbell to a big, unattractive woman, dark in colouring, who said that she wanted her son's ball. If I had not been taken by surprise, I could have said that I had no idea where her son's ball was and indeed did not know that she had a son. This would

173

not have involved me in telling a lie, but what I said was that the ball was no longer here.

"Where is it?" said the woman.

I made a movement with my hands which might have indicated either that I did not know where the ball was or that I was not going to tell her.

"You're a silly old man," she said.

"Clearly, you're not a silly woman," said I.

"No," she said. "I rang the police up last night."

As though I had made some show of being about to shut the door in her face, she then said that she would put her finger on the doorbell and keep it there, but next that she supposed I might in that case ring up the police and finally that she was going and would be back in three minutes with a policeman. This is incompletely remembered. At some point, for instance, she had said that my behaviour would cost me money. However, she eventually went, no doubt to look for a policeman. I do not recall whether she closed the gate behind her great buttocks or whether I had to follow her out and shut it.

It is not easy to find a disengaged policeman or, indeed, any policeman in this town, and the woman had not reappeared when my sister came in with her shopping. We did not quite know whether to start lunch. Towards one o'clock, having no doubt eaten his, a policeman appeared.

He was rather a short policeman and, perhaps for that reason, wore a helmet instead of the customary flat cap (it is quite interesting to see a policeman remove a helmet and place it down before taking out his notebook). This policeman asked me if I could give him a ball said to belong to the son of a Mrs Fawcett of an address in one of the side streets off the far side of Jubilee Road, southward towards the town centre. Upon my informing him that the ball had been put out with the rubbish and that the rubbish had been taken away that morning, he told me that this would be theft (I doubted it, but did not say so) and that his superior might bring proceedings against me. He thought

174

he would. If, on the other hand, I had punctured the ball, that would be criminal damage. Balls had to be given back when asked for. If, however, I cared to slip through Mrs Fawcett's letter box an envelope containing the value of such a ball, that would be all right. We did not precisely say that this would be done, but he seemed to assume that it would and made a note doubtless to that effect.

Alison said she understood that people were allowed to live in peace on their own premises. The policeman said that in theory this was so. He then proceeded to tell us a harrowing story about how kids had behaved around his house, among other things terrorising his daughter. Our hearts bled for him. He would, he said, call not only on Mrs Fawcett but on the people next door. He stowed his notebook away, carefully put on his helmet, winked at me and was let out of the house. He shut the gate.

That was my fourth visit from the police. Next morning, my sister priced similar balls at two shops, finding them at one shop 99 pence and at the other 75 pence. In the early evening, she took an envelope containing a pound note and pushed it through the supposed Mrs Fawcett's letter box. She noticed that there was a key sticking out of the door. Next time she saw Mrs James, Alison told her about our adventure with the Fawcetts, wondering whether she knew them. She did. It was Forster, not Fawcett.

FOR A PERIOD of four weeks, there was some peace next door, and I began to suppose that the policeman had gone round there, as I had not supposed he would. I began some writing.

As their unions allowed the "working" class to save up for its summer holidays, there were fewer strikes, though, at its annual conference in Scarborough, NUPE (the National Union of Public Employees, meaning cooks, cleaners, porters and laundry workers in hospitals) decided that from the end of the year all services would be withdrawn from any patient lying in a bed for which he paid (these "rich bastards" would, that is to say, be "blacked"). Jeremy Thorpe was in the news again, being on a rational form of trial at the Old Bailey. In general, the *Daily Mail* had difficulty in finding matter of sufficient public interest to warrant the huge letters of its main front-page headline. On May 28th, it returned to its earlier interest in murder, of which there were a number of interesting cases that day.

On Saturday, June 2nd, the Clarendon Road boys had a skate-board on the pavement opposite, but our Jeremy was not with them. On the 4th, Denise stayed away from school. On the 7th, after voting in municipal elections, my sister and I walked round the block by way of Hassell Lane. In the Porringers' carport, we saw the baby, Timothy, who must have climbed over the wall his grandfather was building. My sister put him back over on to the safety of the path. His mother came out, looking for him.

"He was out here," I called from the pavementless roadway.

"Thank you," said she, and took him indoors.

On Saturday afternoon, she was sunbathing in a one-piece bathing-costume of pale-blue silk. On Sunday, her father was building up his wall, alternating brick and concrete shapes. Her husband, in goggles and a tartan cap, on a ladder placed in the doctors' yard, meanwhile brushed down the plaster on the far side of the house wall.

The Forster boy presented himself with a new ball, exactly like the old one except that its basic colour was orange, not white, but he confined himself to the doctors' car-park and did not reappear next door. The comparative peace continued for a fortnight or so. Porringer went on with his two walls, which, it began to be clear, would not be those of a garage, but of an improved carport, which indeed would turn out to be quite impressive in its silly way.

Pandemonium did not finally break out again for over a month after the policeman's visit, until, in fact, June 26th.

176

On the 28th, the antique dealer's son was next door. That evening, a tyre off one of the smaller plastic cars, a large pebble and a piece of some plastic fitting came over the wall. These I threw back, as I did, the following evening, a strip of carpet, an iron washer and the tyre again.

Nothing is noted for the following week, except that on Thursday Denise was kept away from school for a second time and that on Saturday evening a musical instrument was to be heard, producing notes singly but in harmony with each other and surprisingly true in their intonation. This was at first a mystery, but the notes sounded when Denise was whirling round a yard and a half of rubber tubing, two inches or so in diameter. I should have liked to inspect this, but it was never to come over the wall.

It was Mrs James's firm belief that Denise was a bad influence on her Marianne, and she had several times expressed a wish that Marianne could find someone else to play with. My sister considered that Denise already displayed the makings of a whore. It was, however, the charmingly mannered, modest-seeming Marianne who, on Monday evening, surprisingly displayed a whorish imagination, seeing in the music-producing rubber tube a phallic symbol.

There were two boys sitting quietly enough on the grass, Jeremy and one of the Clarendon Road boys, with the baby (Timothy) near them, for the moment doing nothing, just looking around. Marianne James picked up the tubing and held it out from her (I remember) pale-grey skirt at the point at which her thighs would meet underneath. As this produced no evident reaction, she then inserted one end of the tube under her skirt and again held it out. The boys stared at her blankly. This scene I saw from my bedroom window.

I note that on Thursday Alison and I went to the Lord Sidmouth because of the children next door, but in general I note when they were quiet, not when they were noisy. They were quiet on the following Tuesday and Wednesday, the back gate being bolted.

On Thursday, the schools broke up for the summer. On Friday evening, the Horror was next door, with a bat and a ball both of hollow plastic, which made a remarkable sound each time they met. He himself did all the batting, while the others bowled to him underhand. As he stood facing the Porringers' and Faggs' house and swiped the ball constantly in that direction, he seemed as likely to break their higher windows as our lower ones, their glass being far more extensive on that side than ours. I was nervous, all the same, of a glancing shot breaking one of our windows on that side of the house, whereas it would have needed a ball hit high and with great force to have broken one of theirs.

I am uncertain what finally put an end to this game. It may have been that someone in their kitchen perceived the danger to that window or the glass in the side of the porch or even the outer french windows of the divided sitting-room and therefore told the boys to stop. On the other hand, quarrelling broke out over the Horror's monopoly of the bat. Also, some plastic ball was broken at much this time and tossed over our wall.

At first, I was inclined to blame the antique dealer's boy for everything found in the late evening or early morning on the path outside our kitchen window, but it was presently to transpire that, although he may have been the originator of the habit, much tossing of things over our wall was done by the baby (Timothy). He it must have been who tossed over a large piece of stone or concrete, pieces of coal and various balls, including again his own large, gaily patterned one. He also contributed largely to the shrieking that went on day after day until late in the evening.

Of the various items which Timothy continued to throw over the wall (there no more than about four feet high), I took to putting the obvious rubbish in our dustbin (this included some old tennis balls with no bounce left in them, tossed over, I fancied, not by Timothy, but by Denise). The

178

serviceable pieces (mainly tyres and other balls, including Timothy's large, gaily patterned one) I put into a white plastic bag which reposed on the floor of the nearer shed, the one with a door, painted Channel blue. These I proposed to offer to Fagg or anybody else from next door who came round to ask for whatever it might be, according to what I understood to be my fourth policeman's instructions. Nobody came.

I had wondered whether Timothy's purpose in continuing to throw things over the wall, especially his own ball, might be to provoke the reappearance of the stranger who had once tossed the ball at his feet. His gratification will soon be extreme.

12: Future Simple

I FOUND MY old service revolver, in a succession of rags, on the silver birch carpet which extended into the long cupboard under the sloping roof off my bedroom. I took off the rags, carefully knocked off the grease which had gone hard, wiped off as much as I could of what lay underneath, boiled the weapon in a roasting tin and dried it off in the oven. There was no sign of rust. I pulled the barrel through repeatedly with a rag soaked in the oil which my sister used for her sewing-machine and, holding it up first to one eye and then to the other, found it gleaming beautifully inside. The working parts clicked as they should. My revolver was as good as new. All I lacked was ammunition.

A man I knew slightly in Jubilee Road, the husband of one of Alison's shopping friends, was a leading member of the local rifle and pistol club, which he had mildly urged me to join, as I had more than once thought I might. I rang him up, seeking information about revolvers which I needed, I said, for a story I was writing. He was, said he, unfortunately knowledgeable only about rifles. The revolver expert was an estate agent who lived outside the town, but whose private telephone number he was able to give me. I rang this man up at home, hoping that it was not an ill-chosen time of the evening for doing so, explaining that I was a writer and saying that Mr S., around the corner from where I lived, had suggested that he would be able to provide me with information I needed for my work. The man said that it was a perfectly suitable time of day and showed every sign of wishing to help.

I asked him first what was the calibre of army revolvers, which I had forgotten, if I had ever known it. It was, he told me, .38 (inches, of course), though it had latterly changed. I next asked him whether my character would be able easily to obtain ammunition for such a weapon in England.

"Legally or illegally?" was his question.

"Preferably legally," I answered.

It could, apparently, be obtained legally in England only on production of a licence.

"And how about abroad, for instance in Paris?"

The French equivalent of .38" was, the estate agent told me, 9 mm. This was, however, a bit smaller, and ammunition for a 9 mm. would not fit a .38. A big armourer in Paris might have .38 ammunition, but no doubt you would need a licence to buy it. In fact anything but .22 ammunition, thought of as purely for shooting at targets. Oddly enough, this also was a British calibration, British and American. It was .22 inches, of course. We should have to drop these British calibrations when we went completely metric, unless the Americans stayed with feet and inches. And miles. It might be a good thing if they did.

I did not ask whether .38s were ever used at the rifle and pistol club. It would be .22s both for rifles and for pistols. It would, in any case, be difficult, especially for a new member, to make off with cartridges, at any rate in whole clips.

Human beings could, after all, be targets. It would have to be a .22, bought at Gastinne-Renette's in Calais, where they might be presumed still to have a branch, like the one into whose windows I had gazed during my later schooldays.

Those whom I wished to shoot were no longer quite the same as they had been the year before, when I first planned my scenario, then thinking of it as the plot for a novel. At the top of the list would now come the antique dealer's son and Porteous. Denise still came well up, as did her mother and Porringer, with the disgusting Mrs Forster on the list somewhere. Fagg and even Timothy might be included. With Jeremy I had some sympathy.

However, it was not a question of those whom I should have liked to shoot, but of those whom it would be best to shoot. What concerned me was peace and quiet here. With Jeremy gone, the Antique or Horror would no longer appear, nor would the two younger boys from across Clarendon Road. With Denise would go not only her own tiresome and unpleasant self, but the too frequent presence of Marianne James and one or two others. There was no point in killing from motives of revenge or disgust. Fagg I needed as prime suspect. The survival of his own son would fit him all the better for this role. So my original scenario would remain in force, the only difference being that it would no longer be much on my conscience if Fagg had to serve a life sentence.

MY SISTER HAD NEVER been so Francophile as I once was. Nor has she ever spoken French as well as I formerly had. She reminded me of my intention not to travel abroad or indeed anywhere again.

I said that I felt up to crossing the Channel for one last time. I expatiated on the golden sands between Caps Gris and Blanc Nez, so different from the shingle on this side. It would be nice, I suggested, not to hear the noise from next door for a few weeks of what might be expected to be good weather and warm.

Despite some recent arthritis, Alison, at seventy-four, was game for almost anything. With something very close to alacrity, she agreed that we would spend a fortnight or three weeks at Wissant. My written French was still adequate to a letter addressed to the manager of the Hôtel de la Plage, asking if he could book me two single rooms from the 3rd to the 24th of September. He could.

I also wrote to Jean-Paul Richard, outlining our plans and hoping that on September 10th or thereabouts he would be able to take me out on an extended trip. I hoped also, I said, that, during the previous week, Yves would be able to drive me into Calais. It would be very nice also if Yves could meet the afternoon boat on the afternoon of our arrival. I did not expect a reply to this letter. Jean-Paul is not a writing man, but I knew that I could count on him to arrange whatever was possible.

With my legs as they were and my other infirmities, I did not feel quite easy about even so short a foreign journey, after so long. I might, I feared, have forgotten how to speak French with any facility. I was no longer particularly Francophile in my general sentiments, but then I was no longer Anglophile either.

For the moment, I did not even know what the currency position was, now that we belonged to the European Economic Community, whether one simply stuffed one's wallet with £1, £5 and £10 notes or still needed travellers' cheques. I supposed one could still get these, and they might be a precaution against being robbed. It would be a good thing, in any case, that my bank should know I was abroad and when, approximately, I returned. My passport was all right for another year. I had never used it, but I had renewed it. No doubt one still needed a passport.

Wissant had recently been in the news and even on television, where we had not seen it. This was because the Gossamer Albatross, a flying machine operated by pedals, had landed on the beach there, after crossing the Channel. Its pilot, one Bryan Allen, had been seen greeted with flowers by the American wife of a retired sea captain.

The IRA had murdered Lord Mountbatten, and the engineers were on strike, car workers alone again resisting the appeals of their shop stewards. We gave Julia Colvin a set of keys, with the hope that she might look in every now and then to see that we had not been burgled and that nobody from next door was in our garden. We did not give Mrs James keys, but made sure that she knew we were to be abroad for at least a fortnight, with the recommendation that nothing should be said to Marianne, who would tell

183

Denise. I made sure, that is, that Alison told Mrs James.

My sister and I crossed to Calais on September 3rd. I was more than a little pleased to see Yves Richard on the quayside, looking decidedly more mature.

At the Plage, I found most things remarkably unchanged and some of the old waiters, who seemed very pleased to see me after all these years. In the evening, I went round to Jean-Paul's cottage, where I was greeted as an old friend.

"A bit of contraband, eh?" said my host, when I had outlined my proposition to him.

As I searched my mind for what answer I should give him (for, after all, the gun would be smuggled in), he added:

"But it will be better if I do not know."

Just off the village square, there was a hotel, the Normandy, kept by an Englishman or, perhaps, rather a Welshman, whom I thought I had met before and whose hotel specialised in putting up parties of English schoolchildren, which seemed to me and doubtless to him sufficient reason for not myself staying there. Unless I ran into him earlier, I would, I thought, call on David Davies on the 9th or 11th, saying nothing of my plans for the 10, for he probably took the English newspapers. I might, at much the same time, contrive to make myself known to the American wife of Capt. Agniéray.

I had chosen the 10th because it was the day on which the children in our neighbourhood returned to school. Jean-Paul did not think he would need to call for me in the small hours, for just after midnight I should hear his tractor passing the hotel, boats not there as here being laid up on the sea front. And so, after a pleasant week on the beach and a trip into Calais for my .22 and *silencieux*, I collected my packed food and flask of coffee and went down to the beach to join Jean-Paul Richard for what had been given out to be my long day's fishing.

IT IS FOUR o'clock. At any time between now and a little

after ten past, Porringer will arrive with the two girls. Jeremy must be home already. If I had been looking, I should have seen the gate open and shut, though not his head over the wall.

With rather more speed than usual, I go upstairs into my sister's bedroom. I stand well back from her westward-facing window, from which there is no sign of Mrs James. Julia Colvin has not looked in all day. I do not expect her now. If she appeared at the moment, the only sign of my presence would be that the current desk diary was open at the wrong page. That and perhaps the faint odour of my last cigarette, whose butt I dropped into the cloakroom lavatory.

And here they come. Still obscured by leaves of the Mermaid rambler, the vine, the honeysuckle and the big cherry, I see the very pale green Triumph drive along Hassell Lane from the left a little way past his carport and then back into this from the right. The girls get out and, unseen by me, take a few paces to the left along Hassell Lane. The gate opens, and they come through, the Whistler first, not whistling, and go up the concrete path. Porringer takes longer. He has to lock the passenger seats from inside, remove whatever he may have brought, shut and lock his own door from outside and walk round the front of the car. I see his head in a cloth cap. Then he also comes through the gate and shuts it, but does not bolt it.

I go to my own bedroom window. I see Porringer mount the two steps, turn left through the open doors of the porch and kitchen and shut both behind him.

I look into the bathroom to make sure that no cigarette end is floating in the lavatory bowl and come downstairs, my feet all the way on silver-birch carpeting. I have, I reckon, three-quarters of an hour to wait for the situation next door to be at its best, the Porringers having finished their tea and being in the kitchen, Mrs Fagg, Timothy and the Lamberts having just sat down to theirs.

There is not much to do. I turn the pages of my desk diary

to the right one, that for the week beginning September 3rd, last week. I restore the pile of copies of the *Daily Mail* so that September 1st is on top. I look in the kitchen to make sure that nothing has been left on the draining-board, switch off the useless refrigerator, then slide that door to and bolt it. In the cloakroom, I treat myself to a pee and flush the cistern. I bring out my burberry, ashplant and plastic bag. I switch off the water heater in the lobby and shut the lobby door.

From the plastic bag I extract my hardware parcel. I remove the covering paper and string and put these back. I further extract a pair of dandified, crocheted French gloves. I put these on, take my pistol and silencer from the rag in which they are wrapped, give them a last wipe with this, load the magazine with loose cartridges, operate the slide which pushes one of them into the barrel and replace it, put on the safety catch. I attach the silencer. With *silencieux* attached, I put the gun into the left-hand pocket of my burberry, where it may be reached from inside the coat, and into the right-hand pocket a spare clip for *coups de grâce* if these should be necessary, as I hope they will not. I unlock the conservatory doors. Mrs James is not in her bedroom at the moment.

I look at my watch. It is almost half-past four. I sit down to wait for ten minutes, almost trembling with excess of adrenalin. I hope it will be Porringer who opens the kitchen door at my unexpected ring. Whoever it is will be standing two shallow steps above me. I shall have to fire upwards and a little to the right, afterwards concentrating on necks or open mouths.

At a little before twenty to five, I put my burberry on, leaving all but the top button unfastened so that I can get easily at the inside of the left-hand pocket, which opens both inside and out, to reach what has now become rather a long weapon. I turn the handle towards the opening and put my gloved left hand into that pocket to hold it in position.

186

After a last inspection of Mrs James's bedroom window, I step through the conservatory doors, closing them, turn left in front of the crime-room windows and right down the concrete path to the gate. I unbolt this and emerge into Hassell Lane, where I turn right, meeting nobody but two schoolgirls, unknown to me, who are engaged in serious conversation. I come to Porringer's white gate, open it and am on their concrete path, with our garden wall to my right.

A BALLISTICS EXPERT might be able to tell if a handgun had recently been fired with a silencer affixed. Then would arise the question where the silencer was. So I leave my *dispositif silencieux* on the *virgule vingt-deux* (*long rifle*, as the French so quaintly say) on the washing-machine.

I open the kitchen door and make sure that Mrs James is not moving about in her bedroom. I then open and shut the porch door and step out on to the raised concrete. I turn right, descend the two steps and walk some forty paces down the concrete path to the white-painted gate, passing on my right the side wall of the carport, through the interstices of whose concrete shapes I see Porringer's very pale-green Triumph, but, luckily, no sign yet of Fagg's pale-blue car, Ford or whatever it is. I open the gate, tentatively at first, in case Mrs James should be out at the back, and then boldly, letting it swing to behind me. I walk along the unpavemented side of Hassell Lane, where I am invisible from any part of Mrs James's premises, push open my own back gate (black-painted on this side, Channel blue on the other) and am at what I usually think of as the far end of my own concrete path, where also I am invisible from Mrs James's, by the dustbin, the water "butt" and the two sheds.

I have bolted the gate. In the second of the two sheds, the one with a door, reposes the white plastic bag containing balls, tyres and other items thrown over the wall from next door. They can stay where they are. A fifth policeman may

187

yet be happy to see them, carefully preserved against an eventual request from next door.

For I suppose the police are bound to call here while we are away, perhaps again after our return in a fortnight's time. They could even, if they called here first, regard my absence as suspicious until they were assured, by Mrs James and the Colvins, that we had been away for some time, Julia, if she thought of it, perhaps even producing her set of keys as proof of the fact. If they bothered to obtain a search warrant from a magistrate, they might even borrow the keys and look in here, but would find nothing to interest them. I do not think they will bother. I do not think that, when we return, I shall need to look for signs of an intrusion of policemen.

With a last glance at Mrs James's bedroom window, I have walked up the concrete path, turned left along the back of the house, passed through the conservatory doors and locked them. Suddenly faint, I sit down in my usual chair and put my head between my knees for a moment.

What has just happened was more unpleasant in several ways than I had expected. I shall try not to remember it. I am glad that it is all over.

PULLING MYSELF TOGETHER, I take off my crocheted gloves and put them in the right-hand pocket of my burberry, which I fasten most of the way down. I pick up my stick and the plastic bag. I open our "front" door, pull it to and also fasten the mortice lock. I turn left and take four or five paces to the wrought-iron gate.

Half opening this, I glance down Clarendon Road, doubtful whether I may see Sidney Colvin's cheerful, ruddy countenance approaching, already on his way home. If I did, I should shut the gate and draw back behind the six-foot street wall. Not seeing it, I wonder for a moment whether I should cross the road at this point, continue up to that corner, turn right, cross Jubilee Road and take one of those turnings to the sea front, perhaps the one in which Mrs Forster lives. This would expose me in profile to Julia Colvin's gaze if she were looking out of a side window for Sidney's return.

If, on the other hand, as I decide to do, I cross into Castle Road, she could catch a briefer because closer glimpse of my profile and then see the back of my head if she were looking out of her front, double-glazed window. At this time of day, she is unlikely to be doing that.

There are no patients in Porteous's waiting-room. Had I decided that, while I was about it, I might as well nip in and shoot either him or Mrs Forster, I no longer have any weapon in my pocket.

Walking with the aid of my stick, I reach the Metropole hotel, cross Queen's Parade. In little more than a hundred paces, I am by the *Maple Leaf*. At two hundred, I am by the *Lady Haig*, at three hundred the *Beau Jesse* and the notice-board. Across the road are the bingo hall and the corner of North Street, a hundred paces further along the Sun in Splendour and David Beckford's house, on this side the *Good Times*. At five hundred, I pass the *4 Brothers* and at six am on the horseshoe ramp to the pier entrance.

The woman at the ticket office says: "We close at six, you know."

"That's all right," say I. "I only want to walk along and back."

And she sells me for 3 pence a pink, child and O.A.P. ticket. I embark on the paler green concrete.

Fagg may already be at home. Hungry for his tea, he will have discovered six bodies, recumbent or slumped at the table, and Timothy out of his mind with puzzlement. Not much disturbing the bodies, he will pick up my .22 from the washing-machine and thus put his fingerprints on it. Being a mechanic, he may remove and inspect the silencer. Then he will hurriedly put these things down again and ring up the police, as at one time he was so fond of doing.

They will not arrest him at once. They will certainly ask

189

him to go along with them to the station and make a statement.

I am tired. My chest and jaw ache. But I have completed the four hundred and fifty paces along the pier and reached the ladies' and gents' conveniences.

To the left, I descend sixteen concrete steps, turn and descend sixteen more to where, on a tide as low as this morning's, a smiling Jean-Paul Richard holds the boat steady with his fingertips on the landing. With my stick helping, I step aboard not too stupidly. I sit down amidships. Jean-Paul starts his engine. He sets his course towards where the lighthouse on Cap Gris Nez will presently start blinking. My gloves and a few spare cartridges go overboard while his back is turned.

He threw all but the largest mackerel back. He has a nice catch of turbot and Dover soles, which he will be able to sell at the Bellevue, the Plage and perhaps (even, without mentioning me, at the Normandy. Presenting a nice pair of Dover soles to the *chef de cuisine* at the Plage, I shall proudly ask him to grill them for my dinner and my sister's this evening.

We shall sit about on the beach. We shall take buses or get Yves Richard to drive us to Boulogne, Le Touquet and Montreuil, St Omer, where I shall reminisce about the Rohart trial, perhaps as far as Arras, birthplace of Robespierre and Eugène-François Vidocq, out to the lighthouse on Cap Gris Nez, looking in on the way back at David Davies's museum of Second World War arms and uniforms, kept in an Atlantic Wall bunker at Audinghen, telling him that we have done so and perhaps being shown the British Crusader tank he is said to have dug up out of the sand at Calais and to keep in a barn behind the Normandy, where it is being restored at enormous cost.

Alarming as is the cost of medical consultation in France, I may take my chest and jaw to Dr Coupin, who is also mayor of the commune. We shall coo over the oiled seabirds rescued by Mme Vigneron, and I shall nod daily at the Agniérays. All these are said to be much involved in "twinning" activities with some English village along the coast from the town where I spent today on tenterhooks and without much animal comfort.

Though English, perhaps the massacre there will get into *France-Soir*. This paper will at once assume Fagg's guilt, as English newspapers cannot.

"Wow!" I shall say to Alison. "He's done it at last. The worm has turned."

"What worm, Harold dear?"

"Fagg. Do try and read this."

And my sister will doubtless say that she supposes we could have seen it coming. How nice that it happened while we were away.

ON THE 24TH, we shall return to that town and to a house next door to the scene of a massacre which had interested newspaper readers for a few days and would do so again when the case came up for trial. The first thing I shall notice will be that the two cars still stand in the carport, where no doubt they will remain until court proceedings are over, both criminal and civil. At least one of the cars will be sold, perhaps both with the house. I shall be glad to see them gone. The house next door at the back will, meanwhile, be empty, blessedly empty, as it had been for the first ten months of our life there.

As I flick open and put away my passport, I shall think again what a pity it is that passport control no longer date-stamps passports on either side of the Channel. It must make things so much more difficult for the police, who can neither alibi a man from his passport nor prove that he was abroad when he ought not to have been. There must be all kinds of people who have been camping and moving on all the time and nowhere near a hotel, so that they no longer have any traceable contacts and can no longer even prove that they were or be proved to have been in a particular country on a given date. Me, I shall be all right in this respect, though the only evidence the police initially have that I was abroad on September the 10th will be the Colvins' and Mrs James's belief that I was.

We shall call on the Colvins that evening, drink some of their sherry and hear the astonishing news. Despite my supposition about *France-Soir* and the conversation I imagined, it may still in fact be all news to Alison.

The police will certainly have visited close neighbours in order to ask them whether they had seen or heard anything. They will have rung our doorbell more than once, but, having been assured that we were in France, they will have established for themselves that we were away and so could have seen and heard nothing. They may never call again.

I hope they don't. If they do, I hope they won't ask me too many questions. I am a bad liar.

They have their case against Fagg, based on fingerprints, the survival of his own child, his prevarication about where he had been and what doing on the afternoon of September 10th and the well-founded belief that most murders take place within the family. Clearly, it cannot have been a burglar surprised at work.

From her front, double-glazed window in Jubilee Road, Julia may even have seen Fagg being led away. If she did, she will seem ashamed of the fact, as though it showed her to be a curtain-peeper.

Dear Julia, she is one of the nicest women, certainly no curtain-peeper. Mrs James is nice, too, but will show no shame if, from her first floor across Hassell Lane, she saw the victims removed on stretchers after dusk. Six stretchers or perhaps only two, each used three times. Mrs James will come round to us when she sees our back-room light on later in the evening.